DESIGN OF
LIQUID, SOLID, AND HYBRID
ROCKETS

DESIGN OF
LIQUID, SOLID, AND HYBRID ROCKETS

DR. ROBERT L. PETERS

HAYDEN BOOK COMPANY, INC., NEW YORK
a division of HAYDEN PUBLISHING COMPANY, INC.

DEDICATION

To my devoted wife,

ElizabethJane

Introduction

This volume presents the essentials of solid, liquid, and hybrid rocket design in a manner that utilizes charts to the utmost and minimizes text. The nomographs have been prepared for use in preliminary design and parametric studies.

Although this book was originally intended for engineers, technicians, and supporting personnel engaged in rocket design, surveys of the aerospace industry have indicated a much wider usage, including management; both the practicing aerospace technologist and administrative personnel can effectively take advantage of it. Further, it should be quite useful as a supplementary classroom text. The book, then, is intended as an aid to the applied scientist, the aerospace engineer, officers of the military services, executive management, educators, and students.

For the practicing engineer this volume provides a handbook and a calculating system. The nomograph series in each chapter provides a method that eliminates gross errors possible with other techniques of computation and reduces tedious and repetitive calculations. Design time is reduced to a minimum, and the engineer's mind is freed for creative thinking. Using this volume as an engineering handbook, the engineer trained for a specific aerospace field will gain a greater over-all understanding of rocket design.

Management utilization of this book allows familiarization with rocket terminology and a grasp of theory through graphical means. Officers of the military services who may be requested to become acquainted with rocket technology on a "crash" basis may utilize this book for that purpose. Educators can use it to supplement standard classroom texts. The graphs have obvious uses in graduate level courses. They allow the student to obtain experience with problems and parameters rapidly.

While the value of graphical aids in engineering and education has long been recognized, the application of nomographs in series to the total complex of a subject is essentially a new application. The advantages are many. The system optimizes engineering and/or scientific manpower. Error is minimized. Computation is reduced to its simplest terms. A continuous record of calculations is provided. If computers are utilized, for example, for a parametric study, the basic formulas in this text may be programed, and the nomographs used to check the computer answers.

Greater creativity, through reduction of tedious calculation, is the aim of the author. It is expected that the rocket technologist will be able to make optimum use of the nomographs contained in this volume.

Grateful acknowledgement is made to the many individuals, publishers, and industrial and governmental sources without whose cooperation this volume would not have been possible. In that this textbook reflects the theories and concepts of one man, all assertions contained herein are those of the author and are not to be, in any manner, construed as indicating the official views of any government agency or department.

Acknowledgments

The author desires to thank the following organizations for their assistance in supplying photographs and diagrams or making available data on numerous rocket firings and other tests without which this book could not have been fully developed: The Aerojet-General Corporation; Bell Aerosystems Company; General Dynamics/Astronautics; N.A.S.A.; Rocketdyne, Division of North American Aviation, Inc; United States Air Force.

Credit is given to the following publications for articles adapted from parts of this book: *Ceramic Age Magazine, Chemical Engineering Magazine, Design News Magazine, Ground Support Equipment Magazine, Houille Blanche, Machinery Magazine, Missiles and Space Magazine, Product Engineering Magazine, Space Aeronautics Magazine,* and *Underseas Technology.*

Contents

Section I

GENERAL DESIGN

1

Mission Requirements

Thrust and velocity

Rockets are based on the reaction principle: for every action there exists an equal and opposite reaction. If suitable mass is expelled from the nozzle with suitable velocity, the rocket will experience a net thrust in the forward direction. This action is independent of the surrounding medium.

Thrust can be expressed as

$$F = d(mV_e)/dt \qquad (1\text{-}1)$$

which can be written

$$F = V_e \left(\frac{dm}{dt}\right) + m \left(\frac{dV_e}{dt}\right) \qquad (1\text{-}2)$$

or

$$F = \dot{m}V_e + a_e m \qquad (1\text{-}3)$$

where

F = thrust
m = propellant mass
$\dot{m}$ = propellant mass flow
V_e = velocity of propellant at nozzle exit
a_e = acceleration or change of velocity of propellant at exit.

Usually a_e is equal to zero, and the second term is not considered in rocket formulas. Using specific impulse and weight flow, the equation becomes:

$$F = \dot{W}I_{sp} = \dot{W}g V_e \qquad (1\text{-}4)$$

where

$\dot{W}$ = weight flow
I_{sp} = specific impulse
g = gravitational acceleration
V_e = exit velocity.

Thrust may also be expressed as

$$F = (M_p + M_i)\,dV/dt = ma \qquad (1\text{-}5)$$

where

M_p = propellant mass at time t
M_i = inert mass
V = velocity of rocket at time t

Hence the velocity at burnout is

$$V = (Ft/M_p) \log_e [(M_p + M_i)/M_i] \qquad (1\text{-}6)$$

where t = time to burnout.

This may be expressed as

$$V = g I_{sp} \log_e (\text{weight full/weight empty}) \qquad (1\text{-}7)$$

The burnout velocity may be determined by Fig. 1.1.

For more precise calculations of rockets in gravitational fields, rigorous derivation leads to the following expression for the velocity increase of a rocket stage:

$$V_n = g I_{sp} \log_e K_n - gt \qquad (1\text{-}8)$$

where

$K_n = (M_i + M_p)/M_i$ for the nth stage.
V_n = burnout velocity of the nth stage.

If g varies over the trajectory, the average value should be used.

Final velocity may be estimated by Fig. 1.1.

Following are some basic equations for satellite, escape, and ballistic trajectories.

Satellite velocity, circular orbit

The following equation provides the orbital velocity, V_s, at the related height:

$$V_s = R_o[g/(R_o + h)]^{1/2} \qquad (1\text{-}9)$$

where:

R_o = radius of earth (or other body around which orbit occurs)
g = gravitational acceleration of earth (or other body)
h = altitude.

Increased velocity tends to establish a new orbit, which may be eccentric.

Escape velocity

The following equation provides the escape velocity:

$$V_{es} = V_s(2)^{1/2} \qquad (1\text{-}10)$$

A satellite with energy below that required for escape will orbit in a circular or elliptic trajectory. If sufficient energy is added to permit the satellite to escape, it will then follow a parabolic trajectory. If greater energy than that required for escape is added to the satellite, it will escape on a hyperbolic trajectory. This added energy, that is, the creation of hyperbolic trajectories, is required for interplanetary flights. Between the initial circular or elliptic orbit and the escape parabolic orbit, there are an infinite number of possible orbits of intermediate energy.

Time since perigee

The time since perigee may be estimated directly by:

$$t = T\theta/2\pi \qquad (1\text{-}11)$$

Ballistic trajectory

The range of a ballistic rocket in nautical miles may be estimated by the following:

$$\text{Range} = 1670 \tan^{-1}\left[\frac{V^2 \cos\theta\,(1 - \cos^2\theta)^{1/2}}{2\,g\,R_o - V^2\cos^2\theta}\right] \qquad (1\text{-}12)$$

where θ = launch or re-entry angle.

Altitude at burnout

Altitude at burnout can be estimated by the following equation:

$$h_c = g t I_{sp} - \left[\frac{g t I_{sp}[W_i \log(W/W_i)]}{(W - W_i)}\right] - g t^2/2 \qquad (1\text{-}13)$$

where t = time of powered flight.

Total altitude

Total altitude can be estimated by the following equation:

$$h_t = [g(I_{sp}^2)/2][\log(W/W_i)]^2 + g t I_{sp} - \left[\frac{g t I_{sp} W \log(W/W_i)}{(W - W_i)}\right] \qquad (1\text{-}14)$$

Orbital parameters

Exact determination of orbital parameters is a complex process including the approximate solution of several many-body problems, but values suitable for preliminary design can be determined from nomographs.

Using the orbital relationships illustrated in Fig. 1.2 for both circular and noncircular orbits, velocities, periods, and related orbital parameters may be established by using Figs. 1.3 through 1.10. The effective gravitational acceleration can be established from Fig. 1.11. In determining the parameters for a noncircular orbit, first the circular orbit parameters are established for the perigee height and then these are converted to elliptical parameters. Use of these charts is best illustrated by examples.

Example: The Mercury-Atlas MA-6 flight was planned as a circular orbit at 100 miles. What was the required orbit velocity? The period? What would the escape velocity be? (See Fig. 1.12.)

From Fig. 1.5, $f(R)$, the radius function, read from the centerline, is established as about $2.6(10^{-2})$ by drawing a line from 528,000 ft (100 miles) on the right line to "Earth" on the left set of points. This value is then entered in Fig. 1.7, and a line is connected with the "Earth" point to intersect the orbit velocity, V_s. This establishes the circular orbit velocity as 25,000 ft/sec (17,050 mph).

To determine the period, refer to Fig. 1.6. First the $f(R)$ value is entered in the line at right, and "Earth" is selected at left. These values are connected to intersect line I. This reference point is then connected with the orbit velocity on line V_s to intersect the answer on the T line. The period is read as 5,600 sec.

The escape velocity, V_{es}, is established from Fig. 1.3 as about 35,000 ft/sec.

Example: If the injection velocity, V_i, exceeds the orbital velocity, an elliptical orbit will be established for this flight. For purposes of this example, consider the injection velocity as 30,000 ft/sec. Determine the apogee, the period, the distance traveled per cycle, and the effect of gravity.

To establish the elliptical orbit parameters, first establish K_v, the orbit velocity constant, from Fig. 1.4. When 35,000 is entered on the V_{es} line and 30,000 on the V_i line, K_v is read as 1.7.

Next the apogee function, $f(R')$, is established in order that the apogee may be determined. From Fig. 1.9, $f(R')$ is approximated as 1.75. This value entered in Fig. 1.5 gives the height of apogee, h_a, as about 34,000,000 ft (6,440 miles).

The period is determined from Fig. 1.8 by entering K_v on the left at 1.7 and the circular period, T, on the right at 5,600 sec. to read the T_e value as 15,300 sec.

The distance traveled per cycle is determined in Fig. 1.10 as 229,000,000 ft by entering the ratio of $(R + h_p)/(R + h_a)$ as 0.4 on the right side and $(R + h_p)$ as 21,428,000 ft (h_p = height at perigee).

The effect of gravity at h_a is determined as 4.5 ft/sec by entering $f(R)$ at 1.75 in Fig. 1.11 and connecting this to "Earth."

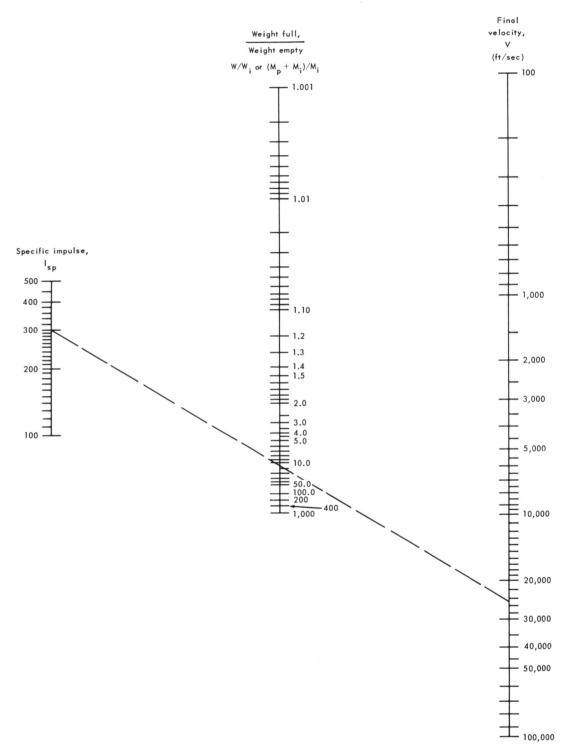

Fig. 1.1.   Final velocity

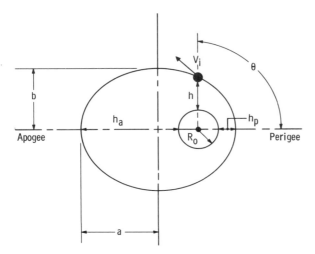

Fig. 1.2. Orbit relationships

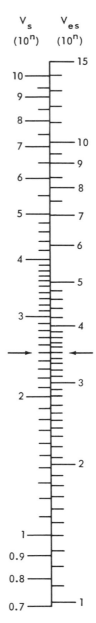

Fig. 1.3. Circular orbit and escape velocities

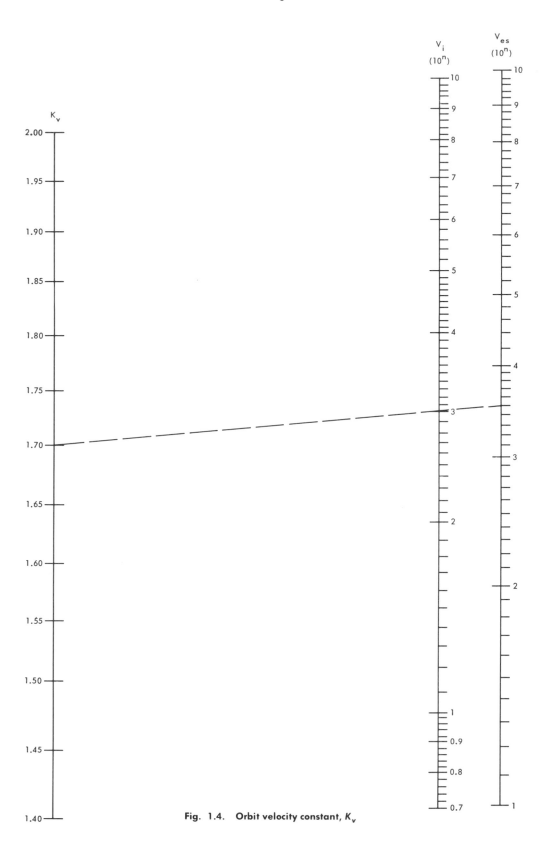

Fig. 1.4. Orbit velocity constant, K_v

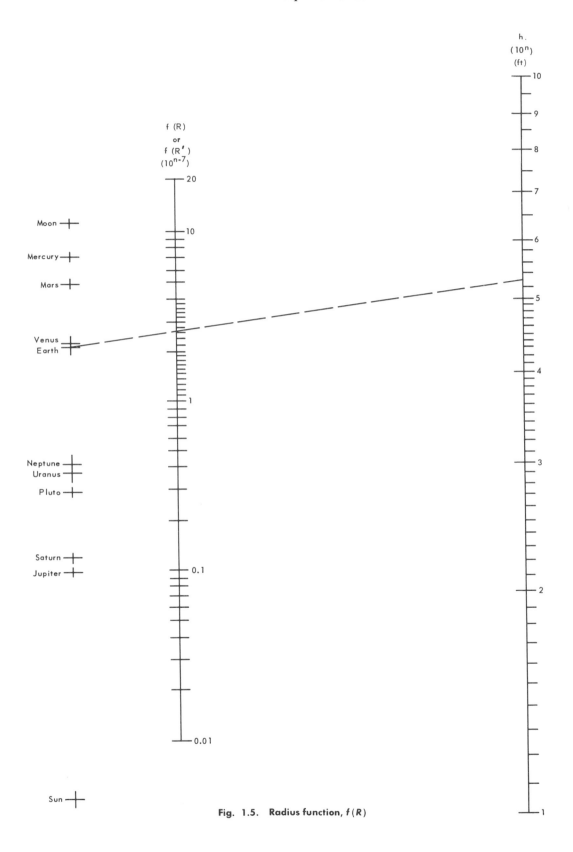

Fig. 1.5. Radius function, $f(R)$

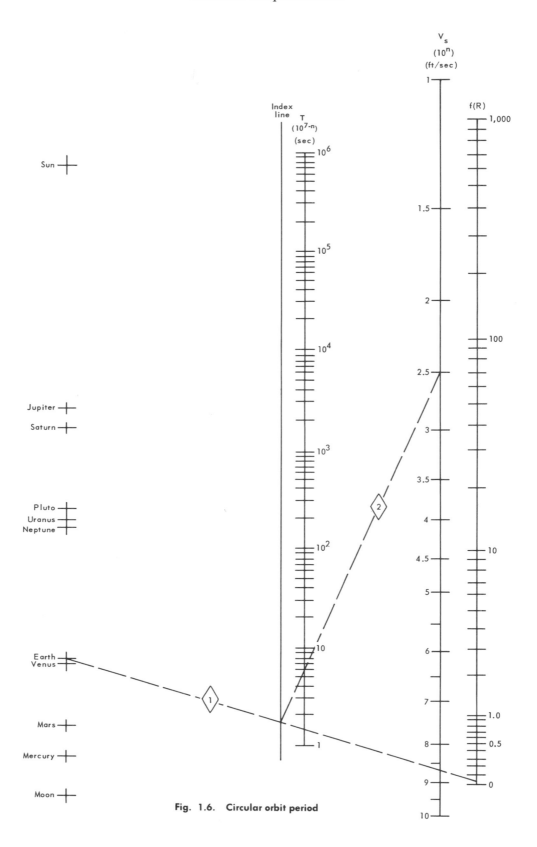

Fig. 1.6. Circular orbit period

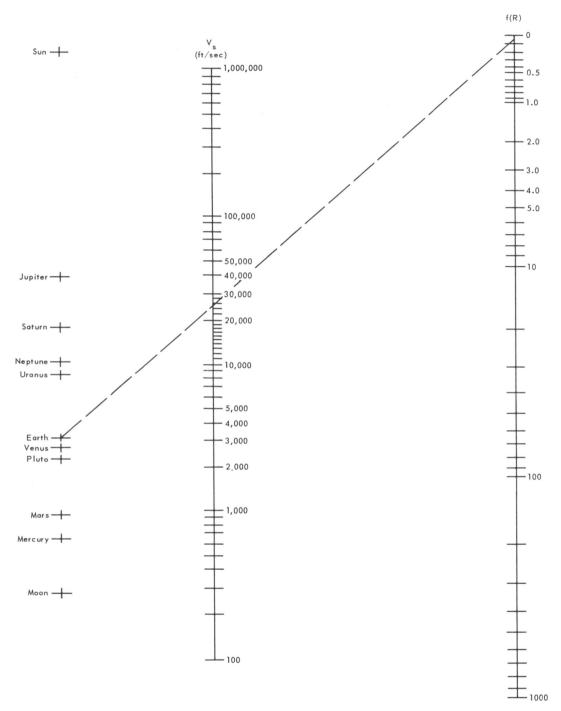

Fig. 1.7. Orbit velocity

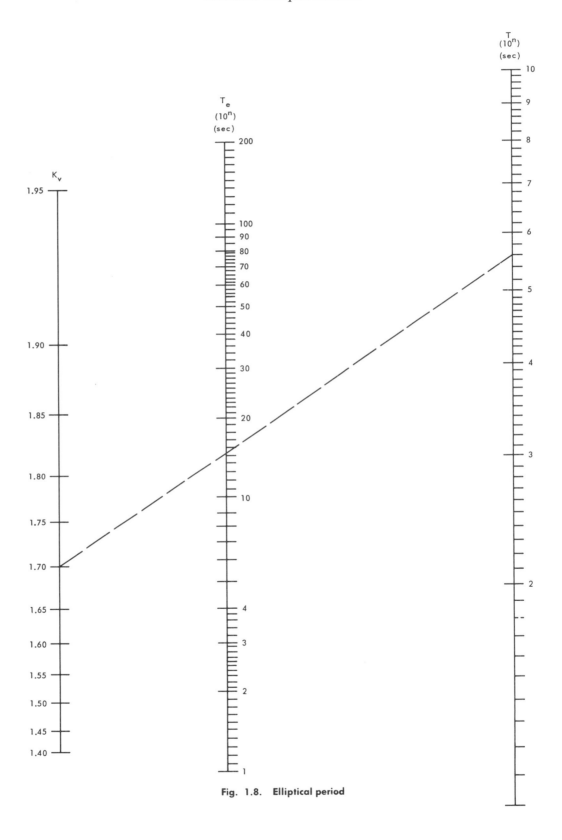

Fig. 1.8. Elliptical period

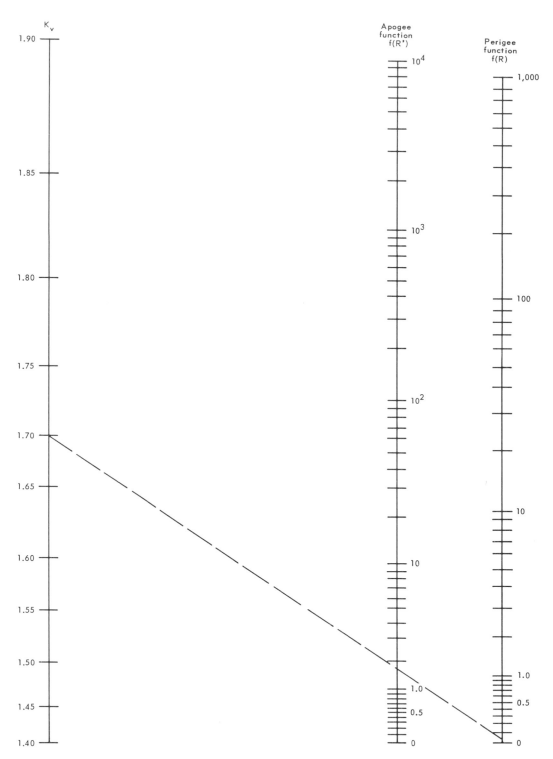

Fig. 1.9. Apogee-perigee function

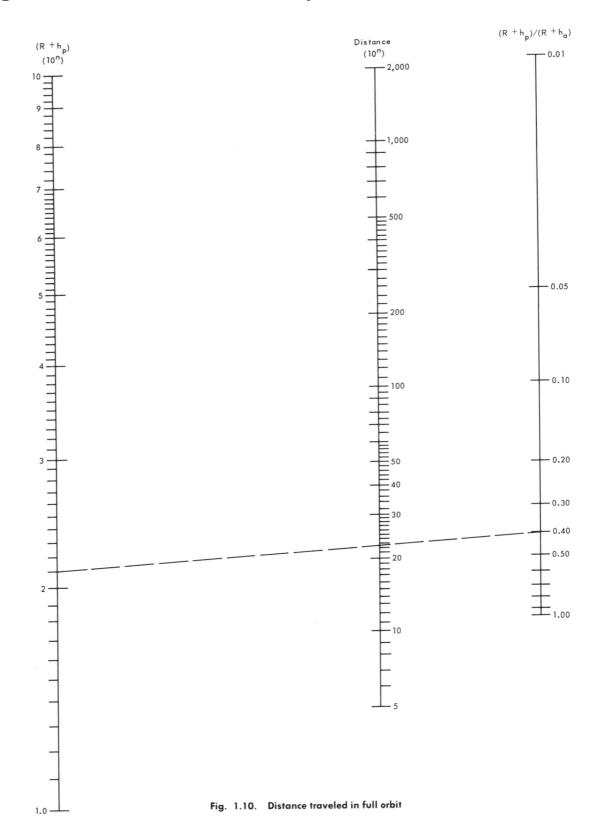

Fig. 1.10.   Distance traveled in full orbit

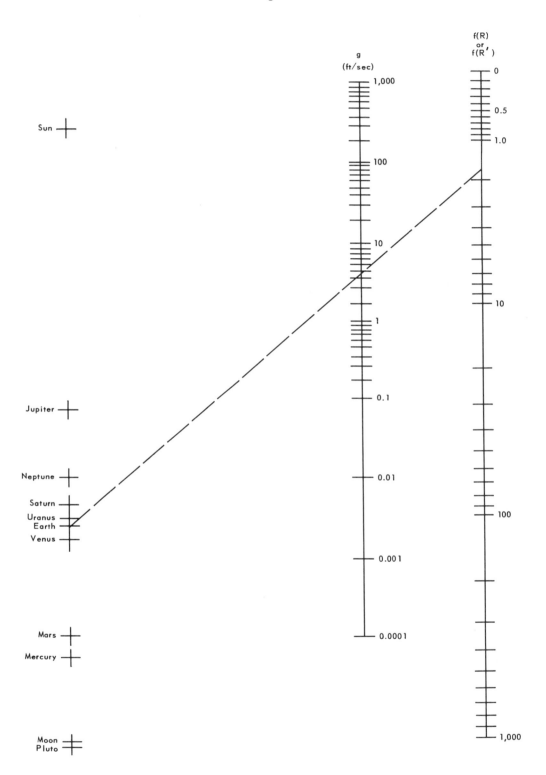

Fig. 1.11. Gravity

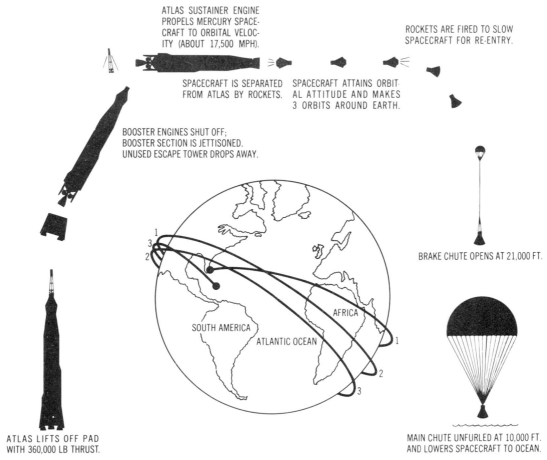

ATLAS SUSTAINER ENGINE PROPELS MERCURY SPACE-CRAFT TO ORBITAL VELOC-ITY (ABOUT 17,500 MPH).

ROCKETS ARE FIRED TO SLOW SPACECRAFT FOR RE-ENTRY.

SPACECRAFT IS SEPARATED FROM ATLAS BY ROCKETS.

SPACECRAFT ATTAINS ORBIT-AL ATTITUDE AND MAKES 3 ORBITS AROUND EARTH.

BOOSTER ENGINES SHUT OFF; BOOSTER SECTION IS JETTISONED. UNUSED ESCAPE TOWER DROPS AWAY.

BRAKE CHUTE OPENS AT 21,000 FT.

AFRICA

SOUTH AMERICA

ATLANTIC OCEAN

ATLAS LIFTS OFF PAD WITH 360,000 LB THRUST.

MAIN CHUTE UNFURLED AT 10,000 FT. AND LOWERS SPACECRAFT TO OCEAN.

Fig. 1.12.   Sequence of events during oribtal flight

2

General Design Relationships

Certain relationships hold equally true for liquid, solid, and hybrid rockets. The specific impulse, the chamber pressure, and general combustion relationships may be considered independently of the specific type of rocket.

The thrust-pressure relationship is shown in Fig. 2.1. The thrust–weight flow–specific impulse relationship ($F = \dot{W} I_{sp}$) is shown in Fig. 2.2. Relationships of nozzle throat area, flow coefficient, chamber pressure, and weight flow ($\dot{W} = C_w A_t P_c$) are shown in Fig. 2.3. The basic relationship of thrust coefficient, flow coefficient, and specific impulse appears in Fig. 2.4. Figure 2.5 gives the fundamental relationship between the ratio of specific heats and the chamber to exit pressure as they affect the ratio of exit to throat areas. Figure 2.6 indicates how this affects the thrust coefficient. Figure 2.7, the flow coefficient nomograph, allows determination of the flow coefficient given the flame temperature, the molecular weight of the combustion products, and the ratio of specific heats.

Figure 2.6 is rather complex. To use it, follow these three steps:

1. Select the ambient pressure on the P_a line, the exit pressure on the P_e line, and connect these to intersect a reference point on the next line. If this reference point is above the divisional line, the P_c and ϵ lines in the upper half of the chart should be used for steps 2 and 3. If the reference point is below the divisional line, the lower P_c and ϵ lines should be used. If it falls directly on the divisional line, B_f equals zero.

2. Select ϵ on either the upper slant line or the lower as indicated by the position of the reference point. Connect this point and the reference point to intersect the left index line with a reference point.

3. Select the chamber pressure on the P_c slant line, either upper or lower as indicated by the previous selection. Connect this value with the second reference point to intersect the answer on the left line.

Ratio of specific heats

The ratio of isobaric to isochoric specific heats, γ, for many of the commonly used propellants has a value of about 1.2.

$$\gamma = C_p / C_v = C_p / (C_p - b) \qquad (2\text{-}1)$$

where

C_p = specific heat at constant pressure (isobaric)
C_v = specific heat at constant volume (isochoric)
b = specific gas constant.

The ratio of specific heats is one of the more important parameters in determining design functions. Its value may be determined by methods described in Chapter 3.

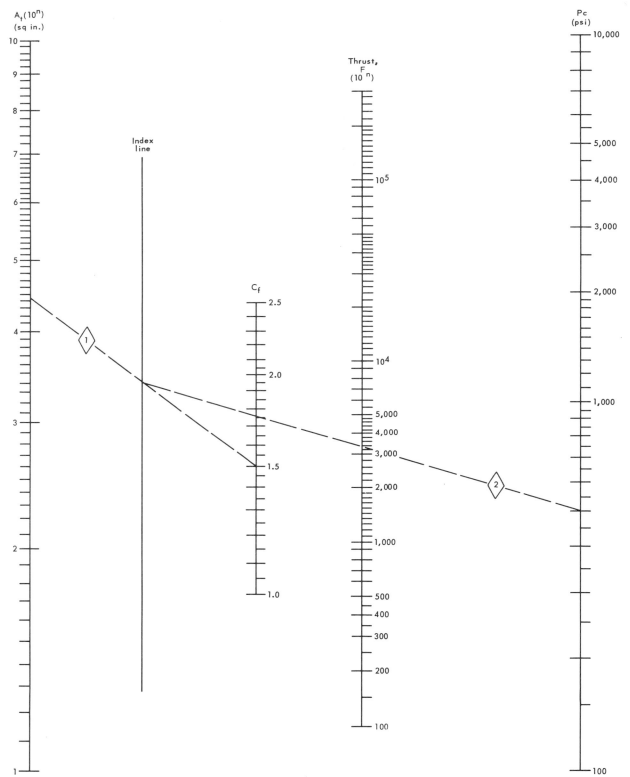

Fig. 2.1 Thrust–pressure

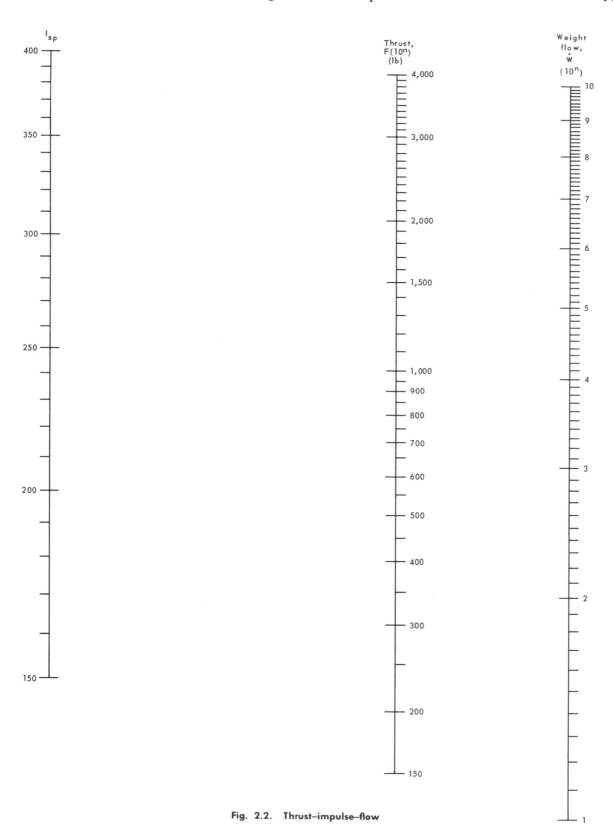

Fig. 2.2. Thrust–impulse–flow

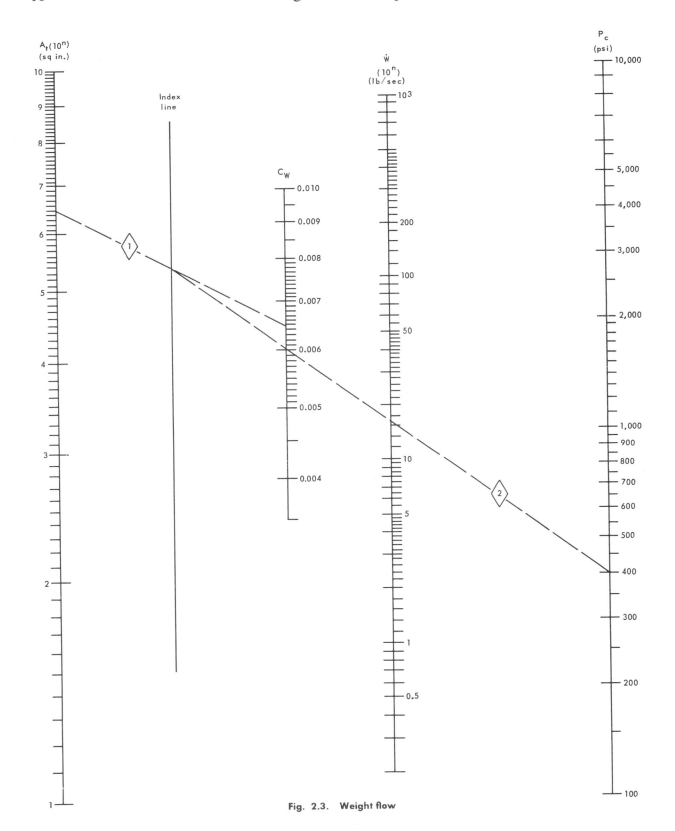

Fig. 2.3. Weight flow

Fig. 2.4. Specific impulse

Ratio of
specific heats,
γ

1.1
1.2
1.3
1.4

Fig. 2.5.   Nozzle area ratio

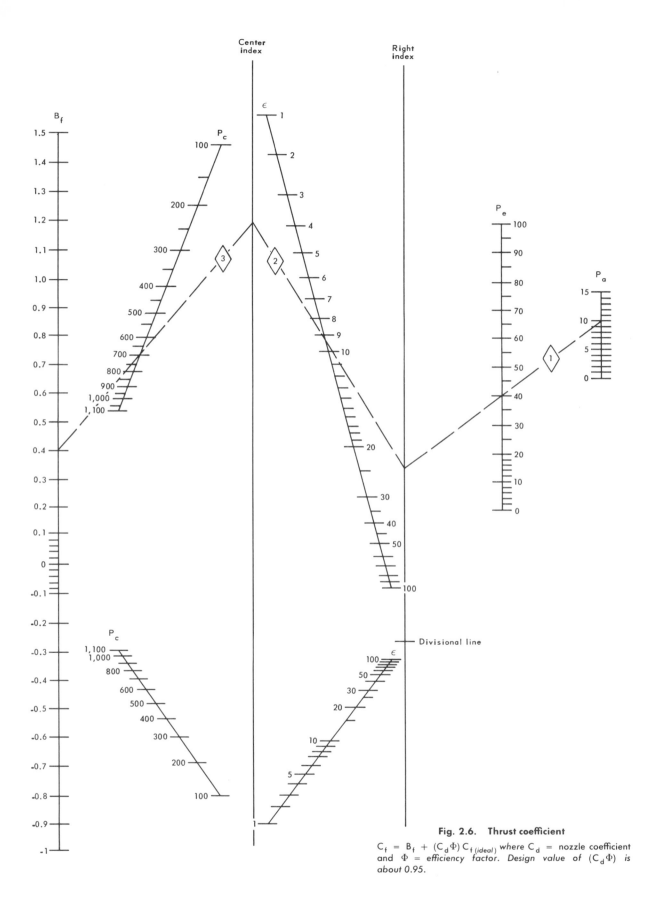

Fig. 2.6. Thrust coefficient

$C_f = B_f + (C_d \Phi) C_{f(ideal)}$ *where* C_d = *nozzle coefficient and* Φ = *efficiency factor. Design value of* $(C_d \Phi)$ *is about 0.95.*

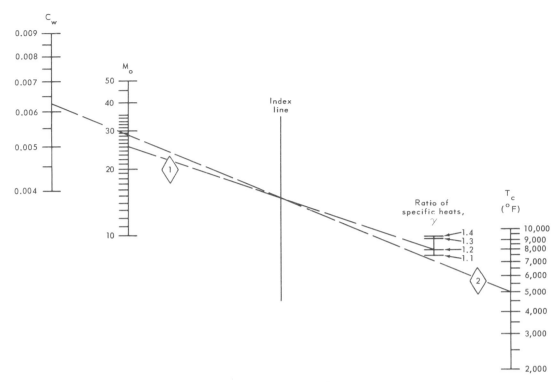

Fig. 2.7. Ideal flow coefficient

Specific impulse

Specific impulse, I_{sp}, is indicative of propellant efficiency. It can be visualized as the thrust per unit flow rate of propellant. Its theoretical value may be calculated as follows:

$$I_{sp} = 6.93\Phi\left[\frac{2T_c\gamma}{M_o(\gamma - 1)}\right]^{1/2}\left[1 - \left(\frac{P_e}{P_c}\right)^{\left(\frac{\gamma-1}{\gamma}\right)}\right]^{1/2}$$

(2-2)

where Φ = loss function = 0.93 to 0.99.

A design value of about 0.95 may be used. For ideal I_{sp}, Φ = unity.

This equation indicates that an increase in flame temperature or a decrease in molecular weight of the gases results in an increase in specific impulse.

Reduced specific impulse

The reduced specific impulse, I_r, is a performance parameter of a less restricted nature than the specific impulse. It is useful as a measure of the impulse of any ideal gas independent of its temperature and molecular weight.

$$I_r = I_{sp}(M_o/T_c)^{1/2}$$

(2-3)

where

M_o = molecular weight

T_c = chamber pressure.

The design nomographs in Figures 2.8, 2.9, 2.10, and 2.11 present a simplified method of computing relationships between specific impulse, ideal thrust coefficient, and reduced specific impulse. To calculate the reduced specific impulse, first determine the pressure function, $f(P)$, from Fig. 2.8 by placing a ruler across the correct ratio of specific heats and the ratio of chamber pressure and nozzle exit pressure. Next transfer this value to Fig. 2.9. By placing a ruler across this value and the correct ratio of specific heats, the reduced specific impulse can be read from the centerline. I_r may then be used to compute the specific impulse by means of Fig. 2.10. I_r may also be used to determine the ideal thrust coefficient by straight-edging the specific impulse value and the ratio of specific heats in Fig. 2.11.

Exhaust velocity of gases

The exhaust velocity of gases may be estimated directly from the relationship:

$$V_j = g I_{sp} \qquad (2\text{-}4)$$

The factor

$$\left[1 - \left(P_e / P_c \right)^{\left(\frac{\gamma - 1}{\gamma} \right)} \right]^{1/2}$$

as seen in Eq. 2-2, relates the gas velocity increase due to pressure decrease (via nozzle expansion) to the specific impulse, hence to the exit velocity. Actual exhaust velocity is about 93 to 98 per cent of the theoretical exhaust, the difference being due to heat losses, flow losses, and combustion inefficiencies.

Characteristic velocity

A direct measure of the ability of the chemical reaction to produce high-pressure, high-temperature gases is the characteristic velocity:

$$c^* = V_j / C_f \qquad (2\text{-}5)$$

where C_f = thrust coefficient.

The characteristic velocity is related to the flow coefficient, C_w, as follows:

$$c^* = g / C_w \qquad (2\text{-}6)$$

The ideal characteristic velocity may be calculated from the following relationship:

$$c^* = (g R T_c / \gamma M_o)^{1/2} \left(\frac{\gamma + 1}{2} \right)^{[(\gamma + 1)/(2(\gamma - 1))]} \qquad (2\text{-}7)$$

where R = universal gas constant.

The cardinal propellant property, as indicated by the velocity equations, is the specific impulse. However, utilization of a specific propellant depends upon the total complex of factors, including combustion and mechanical and physical properties.

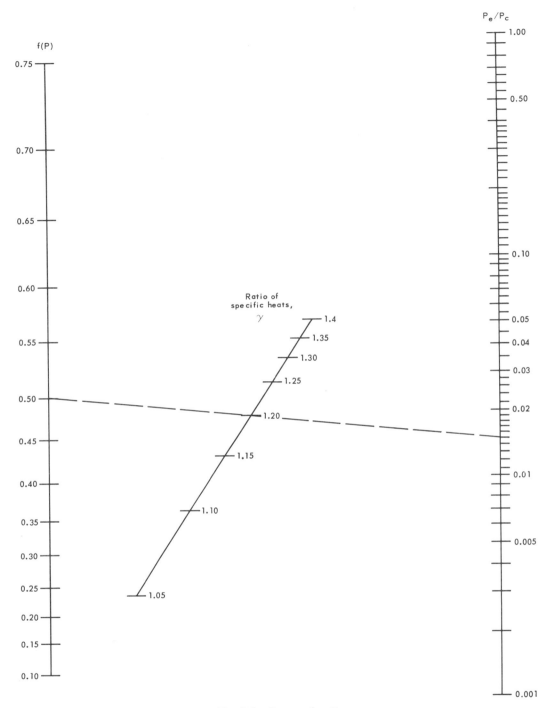

Fig. 2.8.   Pressure function

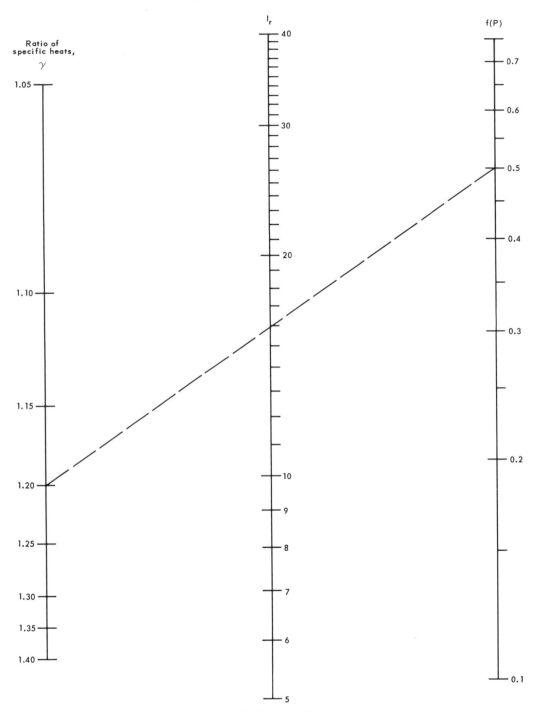

Fig. 2.9. Reduced specific impulse

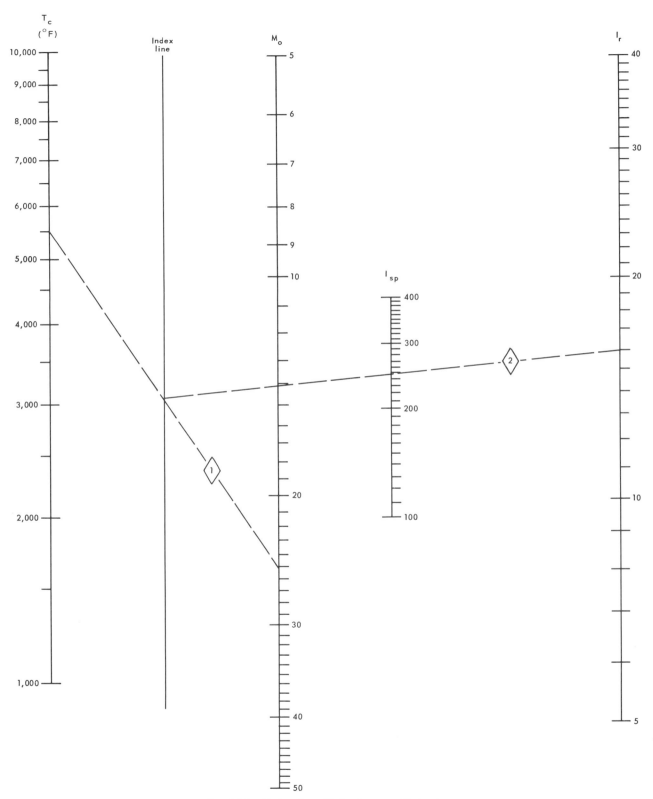

Fig. 2.10.   Reduced specific impluse—specific impluse

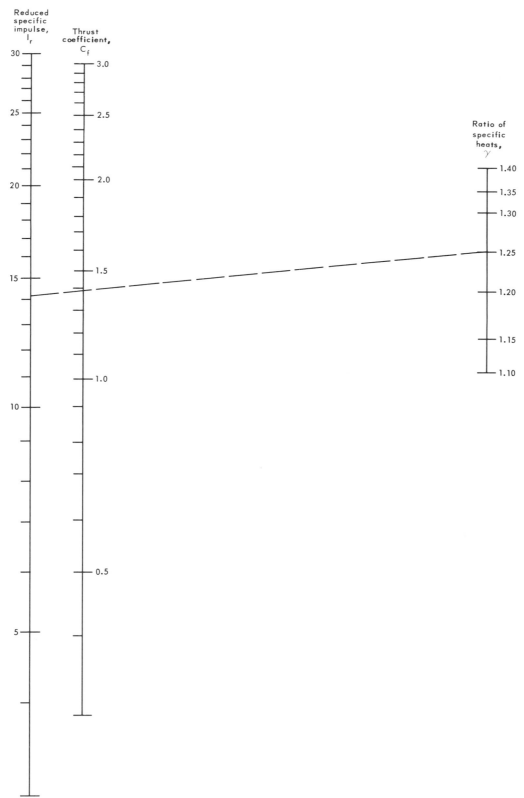

Fig. 2.11. Ideal thrust coefficient

3

Flame Temperature and Equilibrium in Combustion Chambers

Calculating the constant

Equilibrium in combustion chambers is achieved when the products revert to reactants at the same rate as the reactants are converted into products. If we assume perfect gas properties, the equilibrium constant for this reversible reaction can be expressed as a function of the respective partial pressures:

$$K_p = \frac{(P_A)^a(P_B)^b(P_C)^c \cdots}{(P_Z)^z(P_Y)^y(P_X)^x \cdots} \qquad (3\text{-}1)$$

where A, B, C are reactants and a, b, c their respective number of moles. Z, Y, X are products and z, y, x their respective number of moles. P_n is the respective partial pressure.

Experiments have shown that the equilibrium constant is a function of temperature: $K_p = K_1[f(K_2 + dT)]$. The constant can be obtained from Fig. 3.1.

Example 1: What is the value of the equilibrium constant for the reaction $H_2O \rightarrow H_2 + \frac{1}{2}O_2$ at 5,000°F?

1. From Table 3.1, this corresponds to Code B.

2. Starting with 5,000°F on the temperature line at the right, and selecting pivot point B, we index the line at the center with a straight-edge. This point on the center index line is connected to lever point **B** by a straight line that intersects a K_p value of 0.049.

The value of K_p is a direct indication of the degree of dissociation. In the above example, the K_p value at 3,000°F would only be 0.00018, while at 8,000°F it would be 2.85. This of course indicates that such a temperature rise would increase dissociation very significantly.

Furthermore, if we consider the equation $H_2 \rightarrow 2H$, Fig. 3.1 shows that the K_p for this reaction at 5,000°F is 0.028, while at 8,000°F it is 100. This represents extreme

Table 3.1. Combustion chamber reactions

Code	Reaction
A	$CO_2 \rightarrow CO + \frac{1}{2}O_2$
B	$H_2O \rightarrow H_2 + \frac{1}{2}O_2$
C	$H_2O \rightarrow \frac{1}{2}H_2 + OH$
D	$H_2O + \frac{1}{2}N_2 \rightarrow NO + H_2$
E	$H_2 \rightarrow 2H$
F	$O_2 \rightarrow 2O$
G	$H_2O \rightarrow H_2 + O$
H	$CO_2 + H_2 \rightarrow CO + H_2O$
I	$O_3 \rightarrow O_2 + O$
J	$NO_2 \rightarrow NO + \frac{1}{2}O_2$
L	$NO \rightarrow \frac{1}{2}O_2 + \frac{1}{2}N_2$
M	$F_2 \rightarrow 2F$
N	$N_2 \rightarrow 2N$

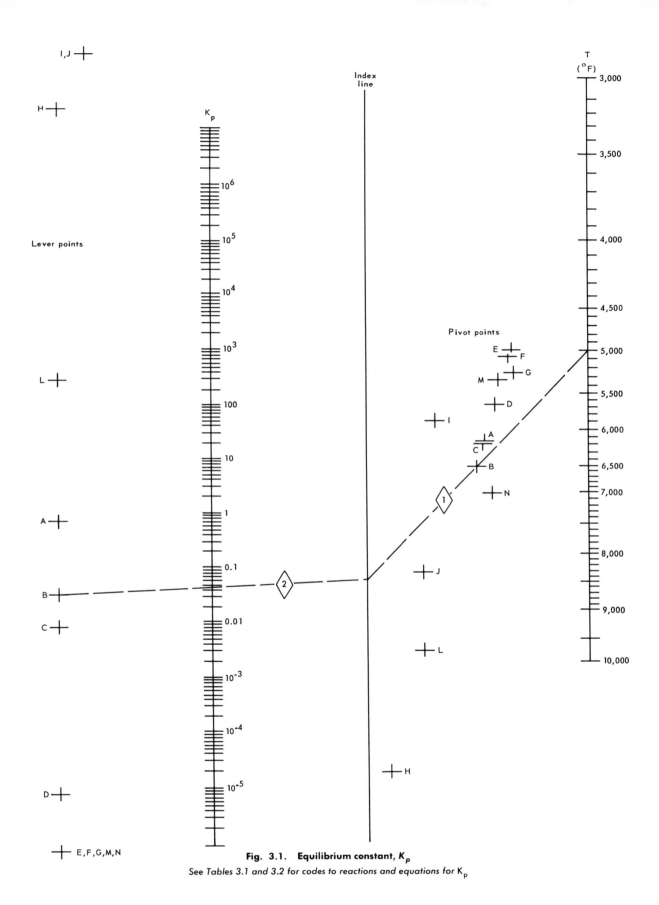

Fig. 3.1. Equilibrium constant, K_p

See Tables 3.1 and 3.2 for codes to reactions and equations for K_p

monatomic dissociation and thus illustrates that at high temperatures relatively complex molecules tend to break up into simpler ones and also into monatomic constituents.

Flame temperatures and mole fractions

To determine the constitution of the combustion gas, we must first determine the flame temperature. This may vary locally in the combustion chamber, but the general temperature range can be estimated by solving the formula:

$$Q = \Sigma \left(n \int_{T_o}^{T_c} C_p dT \right) \qquad (3\text{-}2)$$

where

$Q = \Delta h =$ heat of reaction of products at reference temperatures, T_o

$C_p =$ average molar specific heat at constant pressure for specific product gas, in Btu/(lb mole)(°F)

$n =$ number of moles of gas

$T_c =$ flame temperature.

The flame temperature affects K_p directly. The converse is also true because, by determining the heat change due to dissociation, K_p affects the flame temperature. Neither can be selected accurately in one step due to this interaction.

However, if we first assume some reasonable flame temperature, then determine the sundry K_p values that correspond to it, we can obtain a more accurate value of the flame temperature, which will in turn yield a more accurate value of K_p. This cyclic procedure can continue until the desired degree of accuracy is obtained.

Example 2: Consider a reaction taking place in the combustion chamber of a hydrogen-oxygen rocket engine. The weight flow of the liquid fuel is 200 lb/sec, the mixture ratio is 4, and the combustion takes place at 500 psig.

The possible reactions in the combustion chamber are found in Table 3.1 under Codes B, C, E, F, and G. Summarizing them in one equation,

$$n_{H_2}H_2 + n_{O_2}O_2 \rightarrow n_{H_2O}H_2O + n_{H_2}H_2 + n_{O_2}O_2$$
$$+ n_{OH}OH + n_oO + n_HH$$

The weight flow of 200 lb/sec at a mixture ratio of 4 corresponds to 40 lb of hydrogen and 160 lb of oxygen. Hence, for the left hand side of the above equation, $n_{O_2} = 160/32 = 5$, and $n_{H_2} = 40/2.01 = 19.92$. From this relationship, we may establish a mole balance for each of the elements:

Oxygen: $2(5) \rightarrow n_{H_2O} + 2n_{O_2} + n_{OH} + n_o$

Hydrogen: $2(19.92) \rightarrow 2n_{H_2O} + 2n_{H_2} + n_H + n_{OH}$

The number of elements determines the number of weight balance equations we may write—in the above case, two.

Next, we assume a flame temperature. If we don't know too much about combustion conditions, we can choose a temperature at random in the 4,000–7,000°F range (or in a higher range if a reason exists). For a preliminary estimate, we will use 5,000°F (T_5). Figure 3.1 shows that K_p's for the possible reactions at this temperature are as follows:

$$B = 0.049 \qquad E = 0.026 \qquad G = 0.008$$
$$C = 0.055 \qquad F = 0.018$$

With these values, the mole fractions of the major constituents can be estimated. We can then determine the total heat of reaction from Table 3.2. When we enter this value in the flame-temperature equation shown at the beginning of this section, we can solve for the upper limit temperature. This first approximation of the flame temperature, which we can call T_x, comes out to be 4,830°F.

If we want to continue the cycle, we enter this value in the formula

$$T_N = (T_5^2 + T_x^2)^{1/2}/1.414 \qquad (3\text{-}3)$$

The value for T_N, which is 4,960°F in our case, is then used instead of the original

Table 3.2.   Equilibrium equations

Code	Equations
A	$K_p = (n_{CO}n_{O_2}{}^{1/2})(P/\Sigma n)^{1/2}/n_{CO_2}$
	$= P_{CO}(P_{O_2})^{1/2}/P_{CO_2}$
B	$K_p = (n_{H_2}n_{O_2}{}^{1/2})(P/\Sigma n)^{1/2}/n_{H_2O}$
	$= P_{H_2}(P_{O_2})^{1/2}/P_{H_2O}$
C	$K_p = (n_{H_2}{}^{1/2}n_{OH})(P/\Sigma n)^{1/2}/n_{H_2O}$
	$= (P_{H_2})^{1/2}P_{OH}/P_{H_2O}$
D	$K_p = (n_{NO}n_{H_2})(P/\Sigma n)^{1/2}/n_{H_2O}(n_{H_2})^{1/2}$
	$= P_{NO}P_{H_2}/P_{H_2O}(P_N)^{1/2}$
E	$K_p = (n_H)^2(P/\Sigma n)/n_{H_2} = P_{H^2}/P_{H_2}$
F	$K_p = (n_O)^2(P/\Sigma n)/n_{O_2} = P_{O^2}/P_{O_2}$
G	$K_p = (n_{H_2}n_O)(P/\Sigma n)/n_{H_2O} = P_{H_2}P_O/P_{H_2O}$
H	$K_p = (n_{CO}n_{H_2O})/(n_{CO_2})(n_{H_2}) = P_{CO}P_{H_2O}/P_{CO_2}P_{H_2}$
I	$K_p = (n_{O_2}n_O)(P\Sigma n)/n_{O_3} = P_{O_2}P_O/P_{O_3}$
J	$K_p = (n_{NO}n_{O_2}{}^{1/2})(P\Sigma n)^{1/2}/n_{NO_2}$
	$= P_{NO}(P_{O_2})^{1/2}/P_{NO_2}$
L	$K_p = (n_{O_2}n_{N_2})^{1/2}/n_{NO} = (P_{N_2})^{1/2}(P_{O_2})^{1/2}/P_{NO}$
M	$K_p = (n_F)^2(P/\Sigma n)/n_{F_2} = P_{F^2}/P_{F_2}$
N	$K_p = (n_N)^2(P/\Sigma n)/n_{N_2} = P_{N^2}/P_{N_2}$

estimate of 5,000°F to start the cycle. The value of T_x that eventually results will be closer to the true flame temperature than the 4,830°F obtained previously.

While this cycle can be continued indefinitely, the approximations inherent in other parameters will soon become the limiting factor.

Heat of reaction

The heat of reaction may be determined from the sum of the heats of formation of the products minus the sum of the heats of formation of the reactant compounds (see Table 3.3), as follows:

$$Q = nQ_{products} - nQ_{reactants} \qquad (3-4)$$

where n = the respective number of moles.

Table 3.3.   Heats of formation (Btu/lb-mole)

CO	47,500	NO	38,700
CO$_2$	169,000	NO$_2$	14,500
H	93,750	O	105,000
H$_2$	0	O$_2$	0
H$_2$O	104,000	O$_3$	61,000
N	153,000	OH	18,000
N$_2$	0		

The respective mole ratio is dependent upon the average flame temperature.

Average molecular weight and specific heat

The average molecular weight of the combustion gas can be computed from the following equation:

$$M_o = \Sigma YM_y \qquad (3-5)$$

Likewise the specific heat may be estimated from the following:

$$C_p = \Sigma YC_{py} \qquad (3-6)$$

where Y signifies the mole fraction of species y.

Figure 3.2 gives the specific heats at various temperatures.

Component mole fraction

An example illustrates the method of determining the mole fraction. Consider the equation of a hydrogen gas component

$$H_2 \rightarrow 2H$$

where $T_c = 5,800°F$ and $K_p = 0.280$. We will, for simplicity, treat this example in isolation, with the chamber pressure equal to 200 psi. Hence:

$$P_c = 200 = P_H + P_{H_2}$$
$$\text{and} \quad K_p = (P_H)^2/P_{H_2}$$

Solving for P_H and P_{H_2}, $P_H = 7.3$ psia and $P_{H_2} = 192.7$ psia. Then, $n_H = 7.3/200 = 0.0365$ and $n_{H2} = 192.7/200 = 0.9635$.

In terms of the H_2 initially present, the mole fraction of initial H_2 converted to H is

$$\tfrac{1}{2}(7.3)/[192.7 + \tfrac{1}{2}(7.3)] = 0.0186$$

The mole fraction of initial H_2 unconverted is

$$192.7/[192.7 + \tfrac{1}{2}(7.3)] = 0.9814$$

Although the gases are not truly perfect, it is best to assume such properties for computation purposes. Hence equilibrium

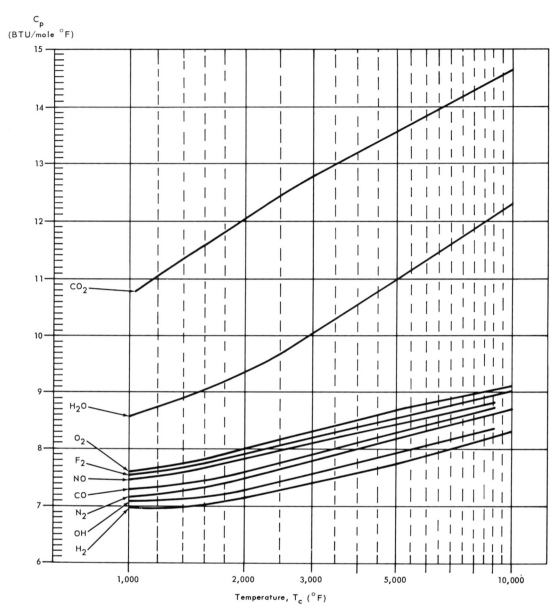

Fig. 3.2.   Specific heat at combustion temperatures

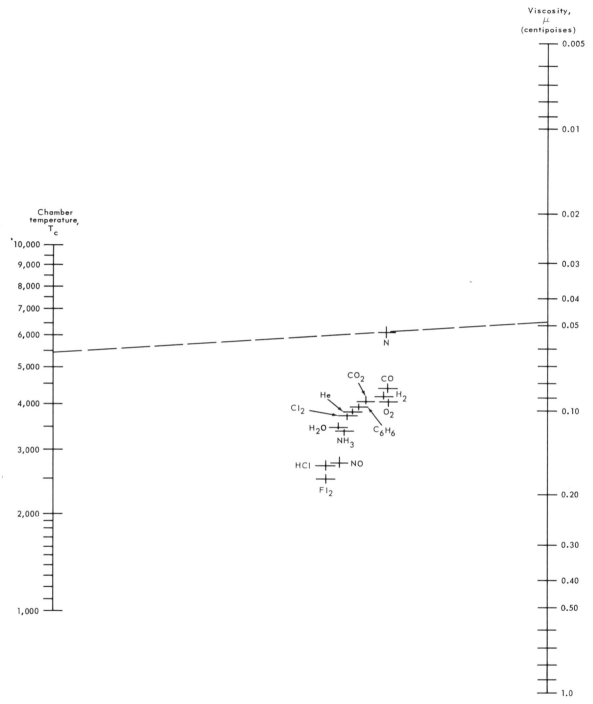

Fig. 3.3. Gas viscosity at chamber temperature

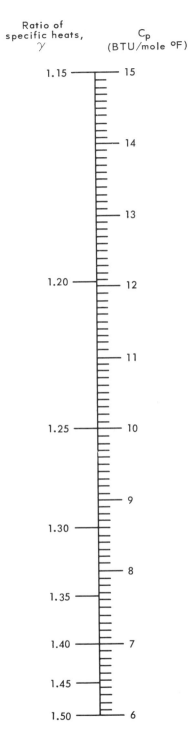

Ratio of
specific heats,
γ

C_p
(BTU/mole °F)

Fig. 3.4. **Specific heat-specific heat ratio for combustion gas at combustion temperature**

is achieved when the products are being reverted into reactants at the same rate as the reactants are being converted into products. In this reversible reaction, the equilibrium constant can be defined as a function of the respective partial pressures.

It should be noted that temperature within a combustion chamber varies locally. The combustion parameters that influence temperature include fuel injection, flow turbulence, vibration-shock, etc. Imperfect expressions for gas relationships and lack of reliable experimental data or chemical knowledge prevent precise temperature estimation; however, average temperatures are suitable for rocket computation. Variation exists along the length of any combustion device; radial variations are also present. Flame front, shock, and fore-aft deviations are further complicated by heat transfer. Expansion of the gases past the sonic point in the nozzle results in large temperature drops. Discharge nozzles have temperature drops from inlet to throat (about 10 per cent) and from throat to exit. The temperature decrease in the nozzle enhances recombination, thus increasing the efficiency of the reaction.

Gas viscosity may be determined for given chamber conditions from Fig. 3.3 and the ratio of specific heat from Fig. 3.4.

Section II

SOLID DESIGN

4

Pressure

The pressure in a motor is an important design variable. Referring to Eq. 2-2, Chapter 2, it may be seen that I_{sp} increases with chamber pressure to some limiting I_{sp} at high P_c (when $P_e/P_c \to 0$). However, other factors beside I_{sp} must be considered when designing for P_c. These include chamber wall or casing stresses, as well as combustion limits and over-all engine size limitations.

The stagnation pressure at the nozzle entrance is generally considered to be chamber pressure. Although such simplification is useful in design, actual chamber pressures should nevertheless be studied.

The relationship of thrust to pressure (see Fig. 2-1) is

$$P_c = F/C_f A_t \qquad (4\text{-}1)$$

where

P_c = chamber pressure
F = thrust
C_f = thrust coefficient
A_t = throat area

and the weight flow relationship (see Fig. 2.3) is

$$P_c = \dot{W}/C_w A_t \qquad (4\text{-}2)$$

where C_w = weight flow coefficient.

The following equation indicates the general relationship between weight flow, pressure, and burning area:

$$P_c = (\dot{W}/c A_c d_p)^{(1/n)} \qquad (4\text{-}3)$$

where

c = burning rate constant
A_c = burning area
d_p = density
n = a constant in the burning rate equation.

Stagnation pressure at nozzle entrance

Stagnation pressure at the nozzle entrance (P_{sn}) may be estimated by

$$P_{sn} = P_g + (1 - K_g)(P_{sg} - P_g) \qquad (4\text{-}4)$$

where

P_g = grain pressure
K_g = coefficient of turbulence loss
P_{sg} = grain stagnation pressure.

35

Stagnation pressure can be considered to be the pressure that would be present if gas velocity were brought to zero. Stagnation temperature would be the temperature under like conditions.

The stagnation pressure at the entrance to the nozzle, with no turbulence losses, would be equal to the stagnation pressure at the aft end of the grain. The pressure is lessened somewhat by the turbulence loss. The above formulation expresses this condition in terms of K_g, the coefficient of turbulence loss. The maximum possible loss would reduce the stagnation pressure at the nozzle entrance to the aft-end pressure.

Distribution of pressure along the grain

The ratio:

$$P_o + P_x = 1 + (u^2/bT) \qquad (4\text{-}5)$$

where

u = local gas velocity
b = specific gas constant
P_0 = fore-end pressure
T = temperature

determines the pressure at any point x along the grain.

Assuming ideal gas behavior, the formulation for the conservation of momentum is

$$A\,dp = d(u^2 A_p/v) + (fu^2 S\,dl/2v) \qquad (4\text{-}6)$$

where

A = mean area
p = pressure
A_p = grain cross-sectional area
v = specific volume
f = friction factor
S = perimeter
l = grain length.

Holding the cross sectional area constant, this formulation may be integrated to the useful relationship:

$$P_o - P = u^2/v \qquad (4\text{-}7)$$

which may be reduced to the above ratio. Holding the port area, A_p, constant does not significantly affect the results of the above ratio equation, although tapered grains, or other variable grains, may have extremely variable A_p.

Fore and aft pressures

The relationship between fore and aft pressures during burning and the changing throat to port area can be approximated by the formula for usual values of u^2/bT at the aft end:

$$1 - (P_g/P_o) = (A_t/A_p)^2\,\gamma\,[2/(\gamma + 1)]^{(\gamma+1)/(\gamma-1)}$$
$$(4\text{-}8)$$

where P_g = aft grain pressure.

Fore pressures always exceed aft-end pressures, but when the throat-to-port ratio approaches zero, the pressures tend to equalize.

Equation 4-8 is a general reduction of the formulation in Eq. 4-9 at the bottom of this page, where subscript g refers to the grain.

It results from equating the mass flows:

$$\dot{W} = C_w P_c A_t = A_p u_g/v_g = A_p P_g u_g/bT_g \qquad (4\text{-}10)$$

where

P_c = chamber pressure
u_g = gas velocity at grain
v_g = specific volume at grain.

$$A_t^2/A_p^2 = \frac{(u^2/bT)_g\left[1 + \dfrac{(\gamma - 1)}{2\gamma}\,(u^2/bT)_g\right]}{\gamma[2/(\gamma + 1)]^{(\gamma+1)/(\gamma-1)}\left\{K_g + (1 - K_g)\left[1 + \dfrac{(\gamma - 1)}{\gamma}\,(u^2/bT)\right]^{(\gamma+1)/(\gamma-1)}\right\}} \qquad (4\text{-}9)$$

This assumes flow equilibrium as diagrammed in Fig. 4.1.

Pressure peaks

The three basic variations of pressure due to ignition, resonance, and breakup are illustrated in Fig. 4.2. The ignition peak varies from grain to grain. It is a function of the type of ignitor, the ignition delay, and the geometry and characteristics of the propellant. Such peaks always occur at initiation of combustion.

Resonance burning has unstable characteristic peaks. This occurs in internal burning grains of cylinder types, such as a tubular grain. Elimination of cylinder configuration lessens this phenomenon. Changing the purely circular cross section, for ex-

ample, to a star configuration tends to reduce resonance. If the pressure peaks due to resonance do not rupture the case, the grain will burn past the resonant subject area and tend to return to a stabilized combustion.

Breakup peaks are due to the physical breakup of supported grains. External burning grains are subject to this phenomenon. If pieces of the grain lodge in the throat of the nozzle, extreme peaks may result. Case-bonded grains do not exhibit such a peak.

Chuffing

At low pressures, during sliver burn or when the nozzle throat area is too large to maintain relative combustion pressure, a rocket motor may exhibit a characteristic combustion resonance in which the burning

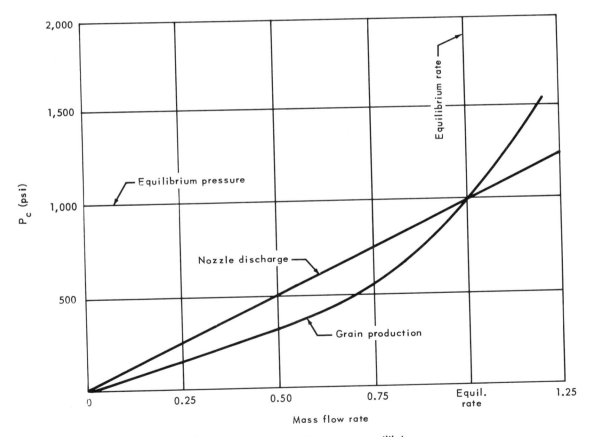

Fig. 4.1.   1,000-psi chamber-pressure equilibrium

proceeds intermittently with a chugging or irregular puffing sound. These chuffs result from sudden pressure rises followed by exhaustion of that pressure. The ejection of the combustion products results in the temporary cessation of combustion. Hot inert parts within the motor then provide gradual reignition. This cycle may vary from a few seconds to more than a minute per chuff.

Such operation is obviously undesirable. During sliver burn, chuffing can result in faulty vector control and thrust termination. Chuffing that occurs at ignition in a propellant subject to malfunction at low temperatures may endanger launching equipment and personnel. Chuffing usually results in unpredictable behavior of the rocket.

Chuffing can be avoided by operation of the rocket at pressures high enough so that equilibrium is maintained and the adiabatic flame temperature and the molecular weight of the combustion products are independent of the chamber pressure. The pressure below which chuffing may occur depends on the pressure limits of the given propellant.

Stagnation pressure at any point

The stagnation pressure (P_{sn}) at any point is about equal to the average of the fore-end pressure and the actual pressure at that point when the variable, u^2/bT, is significantly less than unity, as it usually is:

$$P_{sn} = 0.5(P_o + P_x) \qquad (4\text{-}11)$$

This is a general reduction of the exact formulation:

$$P_{sn}/P_x = (P_o - P_{sn})/(P_o - P_x) =$$
$$1 + (u^2/bT) - \left[1 + \frac{(\gamma - 1)}{2}(u^2/bT)\right]^{\gamma/(\gamma-1)}$$
$$(4\text{-}12)$$

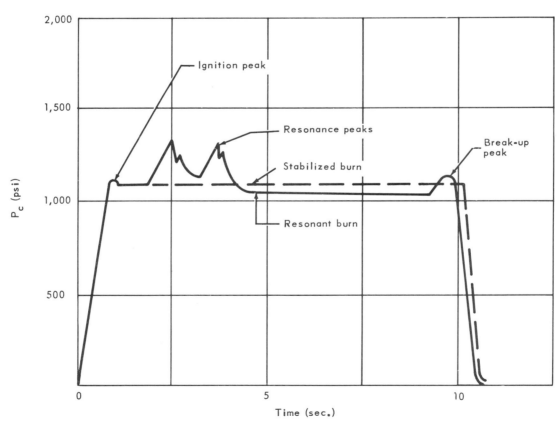

Fig. 4.2. **Typical resonance trace**

which results from equating the formulation for the pressure at any point and the relationship of pressure to temperature:

$$P_{sn}/P = (T_{sn}/T)^{\gamma/(\gamma-1)} \qquad (4\text{-}13)$$

where

$$T_{sn} = T + (u^2/2C_p) \qquad (4\text{-}14)$$

$$I_{sp} = 6.93\,\phi\,[2T_c\,\gamma/M_o(\gamma-1)]^{1/2}$$
$$\times\,[1 - (P_e/P_c)^{(\gamma-1)/\gamma}]^{1/2} \qquad (4\text{-}15)$$

where ϕ = the efficiency constant.

The stress to which the case (or thin wall chamber) is subject is a direct function of the maximum chamber pressure:

$$s = DP_c/(D-d) \qquad (4\text{-}16)$$

where

D = major diameter
d = minor diameter.

Chamber pressure equilibrium is established when the production of combustion gases is exactly equal to the exhaustion of combustion products, as shown in Fig. 4.1. The formula for chamber pressure in equilibrium is:

$$P_c = (A_c c d_p/A_t C_w)^{1/(1-n)} \qquad (4\text{-}17)$$

where

c = burning rate coefficient
d_p = propellant density
C_w = flow coefficient.

5

Nozzle Design

The nozzle must be designed to convert the random thermal energy of the combustion products to directed kinetic energy and, in so doing, must restrict the gas flow so that a desired chamber pressure is maintained. The general shape of the nozzle is that of a venturi—an entrance with a smoothly converging area to a point of minimum area, the throat, then a diverging area that expands the gases to meet design velocity requirements until the specified exit area is reached. The entrance and convergence must be of such a nature that the acceleration to the throat, at which sonic conditions exist, is uniform, and turbulence is at a minimum (see Fig. 5.1). Expansion must be gradual so that the exhausting gases do not separate from the wall. In addition, the velocity vector component perpendicular to the axis of discharge must be minimized.

Throat radius

When pressure and thrust requirements are specified, the throat radius may be determined by:

$$R_t = (F/\pi C_f P_c)^{1/2} \qquad (5\text{-}1)$$

This is further defined by the equation relating the throat radius to the weight flow and pressure:

$$R_t = (\dot{W}/\pi C_w P_c)^{1/2} \qquad (5\text{-}2)$$

Entrance conditions

Conditions at the entrance may be considered as stagnation conditions; hence the entrance requires only a smooth curve to direct the flow and converge the gases to the sonic conditions at the throat (see Fig. 5.1).

Design of divergence cone

The thrust equation,

$$F = (\dot{W} V_j/2g)(1 + \cos \alpha) + (P_e - P_a)A_e \qquad (5\text{-}3)$$

where V_j = exhaust velocity, consists of two terms. The first is the velocity term, and the second is the pressure term. The divergence is described by the half angle, α.

The cosine term relates the loss in a conical nozzle due to the radical vector. Considering the differential of the velocity thrust,

$$dF_v = dg V_j^2 (2\pi \sin \beta \, Rd\beta)(\cos \beta) \qquad (5\text{-}4)$$

where β = included angle, integration gives

$$F_v = \dot{W}(V_j/g)(1 + \cos \alpha)/2 \qquad (5\text{-}5)$$

40

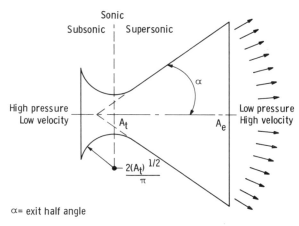

α= exit half angle

Fig. 5.1. Standard nozzle

At the entrance, gas pressure and temperature are high, but velocity is low, that is, the directed kinetic energy is a small fraction of the total energy. At the exit, the reverse is true.

Thus the divergence half angle enters directly into the first term of the thrust equation.

Expansion requirements

As pressure decreases, velocity increases in the exit cone. Efficiency demands maximum velocity conditions and balanced pressure conditions at the exit, that is, exhaust gas pressure should equal the ambient pressure to prevent under- or over-expansion. In the zero ambient pressure of space, nozzles always will be somewhat under-expanded. Figure 5.2 shows the variation of thrust with altitude for a fixed nozzle. In this figure, ΔF is the thrust difference between thrust at sea level and thrust at operating altitude.

Expansion should be of such a nature that the second term under normal operating conditions will be zero, that is, the ambient pressure will equal the exit pressure. If the nozzle is over-expanded so that the exit pressure is slightly less than that of the ambient, an oblique shock wave will develop in the atmosphere directly behind the rocket. If the difference in pressure is great enough, the shock wave will be located far enough to the rear so as to have no appreciable effect on operation, but as the pressure differential is lessened, the shock wave will near the nozzle. When twice the exit pressure is about equal to the ambient pressure, the shock wave develops at the nozzle exit, resulting in extreme loss of thrust. If the nozzle is under-expanded, its efficiency is below maximum.

Bell exit cones

Use of bell exit cones, as shown in Fig. 5.3, to produce a near parallel flow, lessens the loss due to radial exhaust, but the greater surface area partially reduces the advantage via surface friction and flow disturbance.

Flow friction

Losses due to flow disturbances and friction are small in the nozzle, ranging from 0.5 to 3 per cent depending on the suddenness of flow changes and the nature of boundary conditions of the high-temperature gases. The flow coefficient, C_d, usually ranges between 0.97 and 0.995.

The divergence half-angle

The divergence half-angle may approximate 15 deg. Selection of the correct half-angle, however, requires consideration of many factors.

Length of the nozzle in terms of specifications and over-all length requirements of the total motor may serve to maximize the divergence half-angle or lead to under-expansion, hence lowered efficiency.

Too great a divergence half-angle may lead to separation of the gas flow from the nozzle wall, with resulting turbulence and velocity losses. Composition of the gases, liquid and solids in the flow, and possible presence of a stationary shock wave or matrix of oblique shock waves must be considered as related to flow separation.

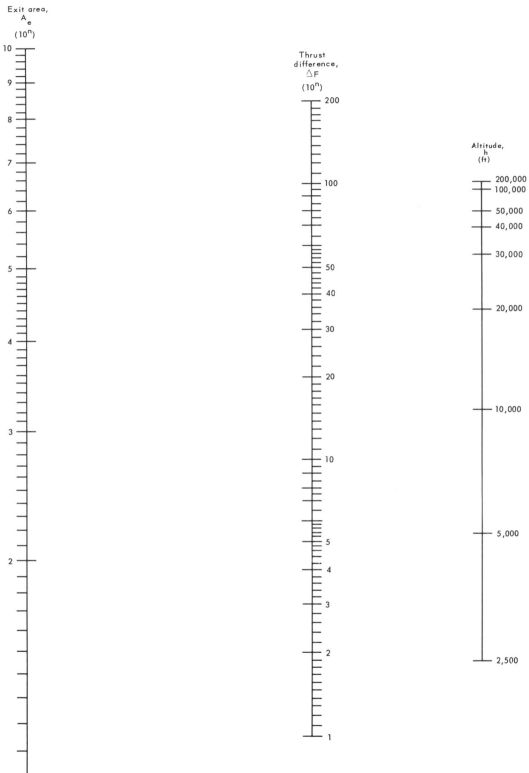

Fig. 5.2. Variation of thrust with altitude

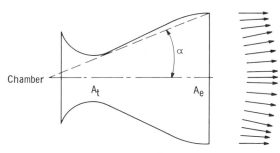

Fig. 5.3. Bell nozzle

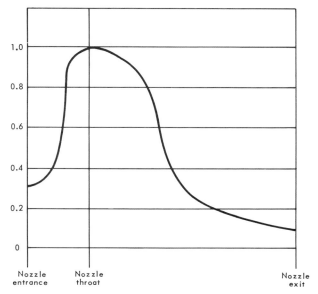

Fig. 5.4. Normalized heat flux in text nozzles

Too small a divergence half-angle could lead to very heavy nozzles and, also, to choking of the exit area by the turbulence of the boundary layer with consequent reduction of the effective area expansion. This reduction is approximated by the following empirical formulation:

Reduction of exit area (per cent)

$$= 0.8L(R_e - 0.002L)/R_e^2 \quad (5\text{-}6)$$

where L = the distance from the throat.

Ratio of exit to throat areas

The expansion ratio or the ratio of exit to throat area may be computed (see Fig. 2.5) in terms of the desired chamber pressure and the required exit pressure (usually ambient) by means of Eq. 5-7, displayed at the bottom of the page.

Heat and materials

Materials are affected by high stagnation temperatures at the walls. High velocities are equivalent to higher wall temperature. Heat transfer effects are greatest at the throat, where velocity is greatest. See Fig. 5.4 for experimental normalized heat flux in test nozzles. Figure 5.5 is a density temperature graph for standard nozzle materials.

Heat transfer

The basic formulation,

$$dq/dT = (h_c + h_r)(T_g - T_w) \quad (5\text{-}8)$$

where

h_c = convective heat transfer coefficient
h_n = equivalent radiative heat transfer coefficient
T_g = gas temperature
T_w = wall surface temperature
q = heat transferred per unit area per unit temperature gradient

reduces to

$$dq/dT = h_c(T_g - T_w) \quad (5\text{-}9)$$

when h_r is small, as is true when the heat transfer of the exposed areas of the case, of the convergence section of the nozzle, and of the throat and the exit cone is taken into account. However, the radiation coefficient h_r may be approximated as 99 BTU/ft²/hr/°F for more precision. Since h_r is much

---

$$(A_e/A_t)^{1/2} = R_e/R_t = (P_c/P_e)^{1/2\gamma}[1 - (P_e/P_c)^{(\gamma-1)/\gamma}]^{-1/4}(\gamma - 1)^{1/4}(2)^{-1/4}[2/(\gamma + 1)]^{(\gamma+1)/4(\gamma-1)} \quad (5\text{-}7)$$

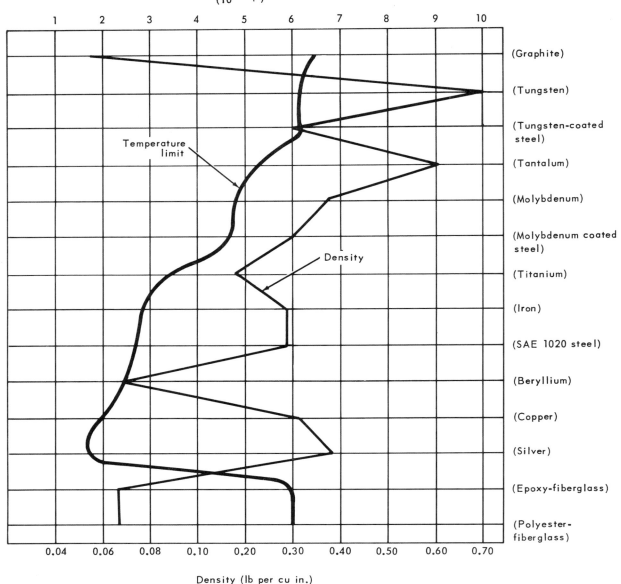

Fig. 5.5. Nozzle materials density/temperature

less than h_c, the use of this fixed value for h_r appears valid.

The convection and conduction coefficient, h_c, may be approximated as follows

$$h_c = 9.7(\dot{m})^{0.8}D^{-0.2}/A_p^{0.8} \qquad (5\text{-}10)$$

where

D = effective flow diameter
A_p = port area.

At the throat, therefore, the dependence of the convection coefficient, mass flow, channel diameter, and flow area results in maximum heat transfer. With the average value of h_r of 99 statistically determined from dynamic conditions, Equation 5-9 at the throat becomes

$$dq_t/dT \cong [99 + (9.7)(P_oA_t/A_p)^{0.8}/D_t^{0.2}]$$
$$\times (T_g - T_w) \qquad (5\text{-}11)$$

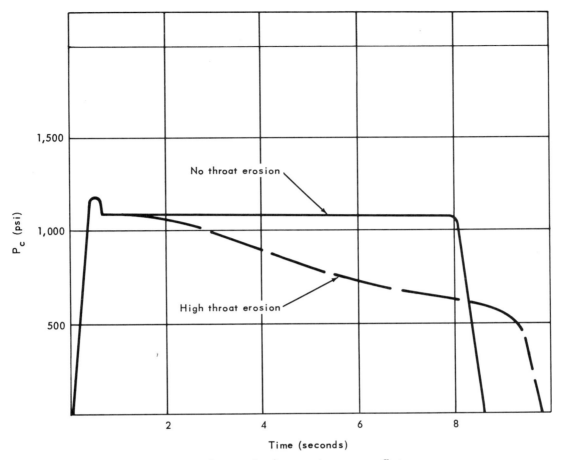

Fig. 5.6. Comparative throat erosion pressure effects

Therefore, maximum heat conditions occur at the nozzle throat area. Material limitations of this area provide the major drawback to increasing specific impulse by increasing flame temperature. Chemical variation of propellants to provide a higher combustion temperature cannot exceed the ability of the throat and other nozzle materials to resist the heat conditions. For more details, refer to Chapter 15.

Mechanical failure as the result of overheating may be expected in many of the inert parts of the rocket when these are exposed to high temperature gases, but when the heated areas are exposed to high temperature gases at high velocities, such as the nozzle throat area, erosion results. Effects of this erosion

are illustrated in Fig. 5.6. As the throat erodes, the pressure decreases.

Stress

Nozzle thermal stresses result from temperature gradients, which are a complex function of the geometry of the mechanical parts and the heat transfer. Thermal stress in the chamber wall and nozzle can be deduced graphically by the Schmidt method, or the techniques of Dusinberre.

Plug nozzles

A plug nozzle operates on the same principles as the standard de Laval nozzle (see Fig. 5.7) but expands to the centerline

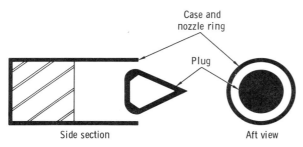

Side section   Aft view

Fig. 5.7.   Plug nozzle

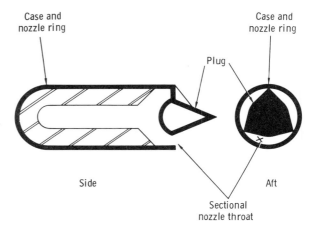

Side   Aft

Sectional
nozzle throat

Fig. 5.9.   Trithroat plug nozzle

of the rocket so that the radial velocity component is converted to an axial component. The efficiency of the plug nozzle, therefore, is greater than that of the standard nozzle.

Typical nozzle temperatures are illustrated in Fig. 5.8.

The greatest drawback of the plug nozzle is the mechanical design of the center cone. This inverse expansion cone must be centrally supported. One method of overcoming this condition is the use of a multi-nozzle configuration (see Fig. 5.9) which provides support plus control of nozzle by a symmetrical arrangement of partial nozzles instead of the annular throat area.

An important advantage of the plug nozzle is its self-regulation with altitude, that is, its ability to expand the exhaust gases to

maximum thrust (reduced under- or over-expansion) for varying ambient pressure.

Controllable throat area

The variable throat has been used to control thrust from 0.7 to 1.2 of design thrust. The variable throat consists basically of two types—the preset or manually adjusted nozzle and the automatic control device (see Fig. 5.10).

The variable throat of the preset type allows in-field "setting" of thrust conditions desired. The automatic control device provides limited in-flight thrust and vector control. The controllable throat area nozzle provides pitch and yaw control, but other means must be relied on for roll control.

Three-dimensional plug movement provides control in a plug nozzle. Fore and aft movement would vary thrust while side movements would provide vector control. Thrust vector control is discussed further at the close of this chapter.

Nozzle cooling

Cooling of solid rocket motor nozzles is rarely done since it is more difficult than cooling of liquid rocket nozzles. A weight penalty results if the coolant has no other

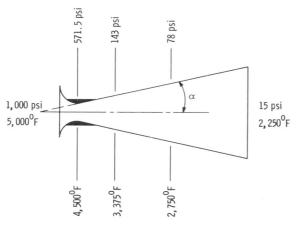

Fig. 5.8.   Typical dynamic nozzle sectional pressures and temperatures based on 1,000-psi chamber pressure and 5,000°F flame temperature

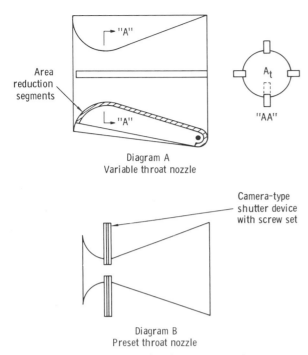

Diagram A
Variable throat nozzle

Diagram B
Preset throat nozzle

Fig. 5.10. Variable throat area nozzles

function than heat removal. In liquid engines, either fuel or oxidizer may be used as a nozzle coolant that carries the heat energy back to the combustion area. As solid rocket motors usually cannot so utilize the coolant, it must be considered "extra" weight.

A coolant may be solid or liquid. Venting must be provided for exhausting of gases produced in the cooling process, if evaporation is utilized. If simple liquid thermal capacity and displacement is the basis of design, coolant weight is maximum. Vaporization or sublimation provides the greatest efficiency.

Nozzle cooling lengthens material life and allows increased specific impulse by increasing flame temperature.

Ablative nozzles and chambers

Developments in plastic cases and nozzles permit the ablative characteristics of plastics to be used to provide heat transfer

control. Filament-wound nozzles and cases have high tensile strength-to-weight ratios. When nozzles are designed of the same material as the case in solid propellant devices or as the combustion chamber in liquid rockets, the nozzle and chamber case may be integrally wound. This maximizes the strength-to-weight ratio.

Ablation can be defined as the process of using heat to vaporize or sublime a material so as to maintain low temperatures. The surface material may be sublimed or otherwise removed and possibly vaporized. The ablation mass flow, of itself, provides an insulation factor as well as an energy absorption capacity. In terms of heat transfer, its effective heat capacity should be considered. Ablative mass flow is directed normal to the hot gas mass flow. This effectively increases the boundary layer. A typical ablative skirt is illustrated in Fig. 5.11.

The heat transfer in terms of an ablative surface exposed to hot gases is defined by the following formula:

$$q = (\dot{W}/A)(C_h)(\Delta h) - \dot{W}_a H \qquad (5\text{-}12)$$

where

$\dot{W}$ = combustion products weight flow
A = passage cross-section area
C_h = heat transfer coefficient
$\dot{W}_a$ = ablating material mass flow per unit area
H = heat of vaporization and/or sublimation.

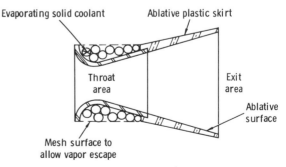

Fig. 5.11. Ablative plastic skirt of typical solid-cooled nozzle

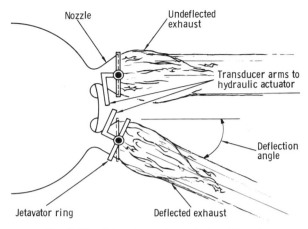

Fig. 5.12.   Jetavator vector control multinozzle

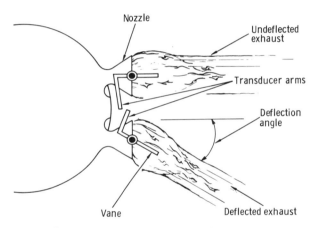

Fig. 5.13.   Jet vane vector control multinozzle

The expression Δh can be defined in terms of a reacting surface:

$$\Delta h = \Sigma_i (K_i)_{bound}(h_{bound} - h_{wall}) + (\dot{W}_a/d_j)^2/2$$
$$+ (K_o)_{bound}(\Delta Q) \qquad (5\text{-}13)$$

where

$$d_j = \text{gas density}$$
$$K_i, K_o = \text{transfer constants}$$
$$\Delta Q = \text{heat difference.}$$

The first and last term may be exactly determined by experiment. The inherent servotransfer characteristics of the ablative surfaces are apparent in Equation 5-12. As a greater amount of heat is transferred to the face of the material, ablation increases, tending to lower the heat transfer. This in turn lowers the ablation, which leads to an increase in temperature and, hence, an increase in ablation. If the temperature is unsteady, a cycling occurs. If the temperature is stable, the ablation tends to reach a state of equilibrium.

Some materials collect a char over the surface which slightly inhibits the ablative process. However, the carbon provides an insulation to compensate for the ablative decrease. When the hot gases are stagnant, ablation decreases to a null condition, and only carbon insulation provides heat protection.

Fig. 5.14.   Pivoting nozzles

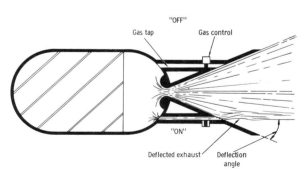

Fig. 5.15.   Gas injection vector control

Vector control

The method of vector control affects the nozzle design. Control of the thrust vector may be accomplished by the following methods:

1. Jet deflection
2. Nozzle or chamber pivoting
3. Parameter variation
4. Auxiliary rockets
5. Aerodynamic fins
6. Gas injection
7. Propellant flow control.

Jet vanes, jet tabs, and jetavators are in the first group. Fig. 5-12 diagrammatically shows jetavator operation. In the upper part of the diagram, the jetavator ring is in the neutral position, whereas in the lower, it is deflecting the stream. These rings can be considered extensions of the nozzle that pivot into the stream on command. The rings are exposed to the heat of the gases only when actuated. Figure 5.13 shows operation of a jet vane system. The upper vane is in the neutral position. The lower vane is actuated. A major defect in utilizing jet vanes is their constant exposure to combustion products.

The concept of pivoting the combustion chamber for vector control has long been accepted in liquid rocket design when chamber and nozzle are a comparatively small single unit. Extension of this concept to solid rocketry has led to the pivoting nozzle. Figure 5.14 illustrates this nozzle (only one transducer arm has been shown for simplicity). Actuation of the hydraulic system pushes or pulls the nozzle to the required angle. Each of the other nozzles is connected to a like system. The major difficulty in such a design for a solid rocket is in engineering the proper pivotable joint between case and nozzle.

In the next classification (parameter variation), thrust variation and vector control are achieved by varying the throat area. Variable throat area nozzles were shown in Fig. 5.12. The pivoting units must be attached to the nozzle.

Vector control and thrust control in a plug nozzle configuration can be accomplished by movement of the plug, as previously discussed.

Gas injection as illustrated in Fig. 5.15 requires modification of the nozzle walls.

6

Grain Design

The essence of solid rocket motor engineering is grain design. A good grain design results in a superior rocket. Poor design can result in a low-efficiency motor. The designer must consider simplicity, reproducibility, and economy in his design. The limitations of available production equipment must also be evaluated. Simplicity and reliability often go hand-in-hand. Reduction of complexity in mechanical parts and the grain will reduce the number of malfunctions.

Type of mission, size of motor, and other specification limitations provide design parameters. Exterior burning grains are superior for small rocket and auxiliary units. Internal burning configurations optimize performance for large rockets. Motors with multi-million pound thrust must either be designed for the extreme confinements of on-site manufacturing or produced in mobile segments for on-site assembly.

Although a totally new design may be warranted in one instance, another situation may require an expansion or modification of a proven design. Economic considerations may determine the course of action and may also limit optimization.

When propellant properties and specifications for chamber pressure, thrust, and duration are known, grain design can be initiated.

The basic parameters needed for geometric design are web dimension, w (thickness of propellant normal to combustion surface), propellant weight, W_p, and chamber burning area, A_c.

Web dimension

The web thickness can be determined as the distance burned, that is, the burning rate times the burning time, by means of the following equation or Fig. 6.1:

$$w = r t_w \qquad (6-1)$$

where

w = web thickness
r = average burning rate
t_w = thrust duration desired.

The web thickness so determined must, of course, be varied as indicated by studies related to erosive burning.

Propellant weight

If the propellant weight, W_p, is not specified, it may be calculated directly from the total impulse relationship,

$$I = F t_w \qquad (6-2)$$

where F, the thrust, is considered essentially constant. It may be calculated from knowledge of I in the following total weight formulation:

$$W_p = I/I_{sp} \qquad (6-3)$$

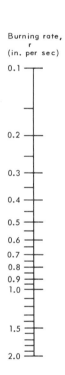

Burning rate,
r
(in. per sec)

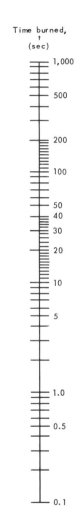

Time burned,
t
(sec)

Web or distance burned,
w
(in.)

Fig. 6.1. Time/distance rate

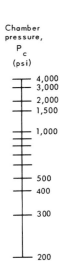

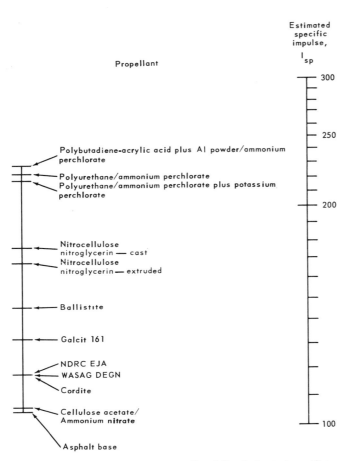

Fig. 6.2.   Estimated specific impulse for solid propellants

The specific impulse of solid propellants may be estimated by means of Figs. 6.2 and 6.3. Hence the volume of propellant follows directly:

$$V_p = W_p/d_p \qquad (6\text{-}4)$$

The propellant density, d_p, may be determined from Fig. 6.4. In the example of a case-bonded, internal perforation grain of the type shown in Fig. 6.5, the volume of propellant would equal the volume of the case minus the volume of the perforation. Hence,

$$V_p = V_{\text{case}} - A_p L_g \qquad (6\text{-}5)$$

where

L_g = length of grain
A_p = port or duct area.

The volume of other grains can be computed by direct geometric analysis.

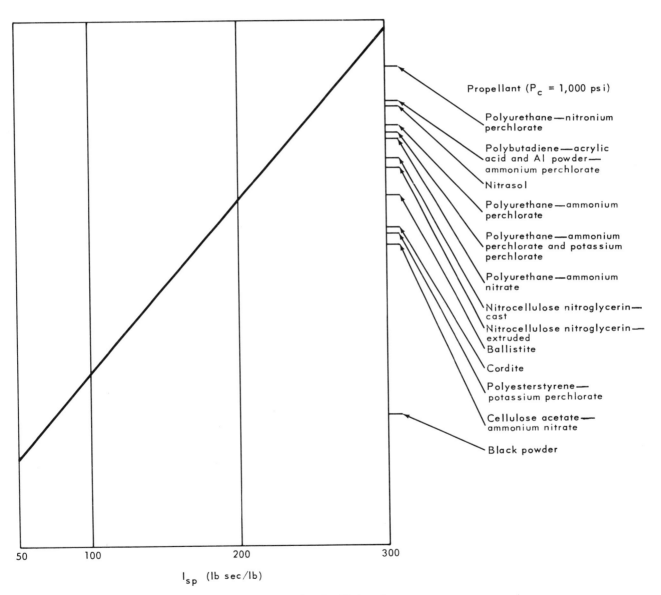

Fig. 6.3. Specific impulse

Chamber burning area

The chamber burning area, A_c, is readily computed if either weight flow or chamber pressure, P_c, is determined. If pressure is known,

$$A_c = A_t C_w P_c^{(1-n)}/cd_p \qquad (6\text{-}6)$$

where

A_t = throat area
C_w = flow coefficient
n = burning rate exponent
c = burning rate constant
P_c = chamber pressure
d_p = propellant density

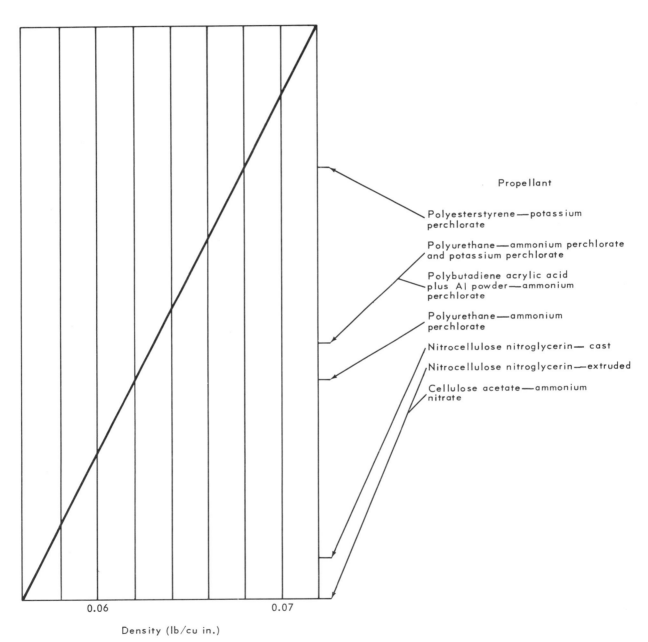

Propellant

Polyesterstyrene—potassium perchlorate

Polyurethane—ammonium perchlorate and potassium perchlorate

Polybutadiene acrylic acid plus Al powder—ammonium perchlorate

Polyurethane—ammonium perchlorate

Nitrocellulose nitroglycerin— cast

Nitrocellulose nitroglycerin—extruded

Cellulose acetate—ammonium nitrate

Density (lb/cu in.)

Fig. 6.4. Propellant density

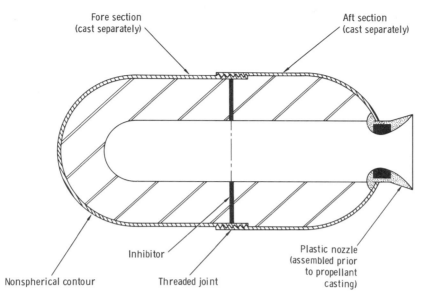

Fore section
(cast separately)

Aft section
(cast separately)

Nonspherical contour

Inhibitor

Threaded joint

Plastic nozzle
(assembled prior
to propellant
casting)

Fig. 6.5.   Center-joint case

This relationship is presented in Fig. 6.6. An example to illustrate the use of Fig. 6.6 follows. With a c value of 0.05, a propellant density of 0.06, an n value of 0.35, a flow coefficient value of 0.006, a design chamber pressure of 1,000 psi, and a throat area of 50 sq in., what is the needed burning area, A_c?

1. Select value of the burning rate coefficient on line c, value of the propellant density on line d_p, and index these values on the right index line.
2. Select flow coefficient on line C_w and throat area value on line A_t. Index these values on line $A_c P_c$.
3. Using these values, index centerline.
4. Select design pressure on line P_c and correct value of n on the diagonal line and index these values on the right index line.
5. Using this value plus the centerline point, index correct burning area value of 8,000 sq in. on A_c line.

If weight flow, $\dot{W}$, is known, the following expression may be used for the chamber burning area:

$$A_c = \dot{W}/r d_p \qquad (6\text{-}7)$$

This equation may be solved by use of Fig. 6.7.

Usually, it is desired to have an essentially constant chamber burning area from ignition to web burnout. If an internal perforation motor were a purely cylindrical shape, a constant perimeter of burn, s, times the length would give a constant value of the chamber burning area. As illustrated in Fig. 6.8, however, the fore head is usually hemispherical or ellipsoidal (aft end often also curved). Hence the effective length of L_g decreases during combustion. To compensate for this condition, a progressive perimeter burning curve is often selected, effectively regressing the curve with a nonlinear peak at ignition.

For further discussion of the design of grains relative to purely geometrical considerations, see the sections dealing with grain geometry.

Port-to-throat area ratios

The greater the propellant loading (weight of propellant per unit of case volume), the greater the performance level

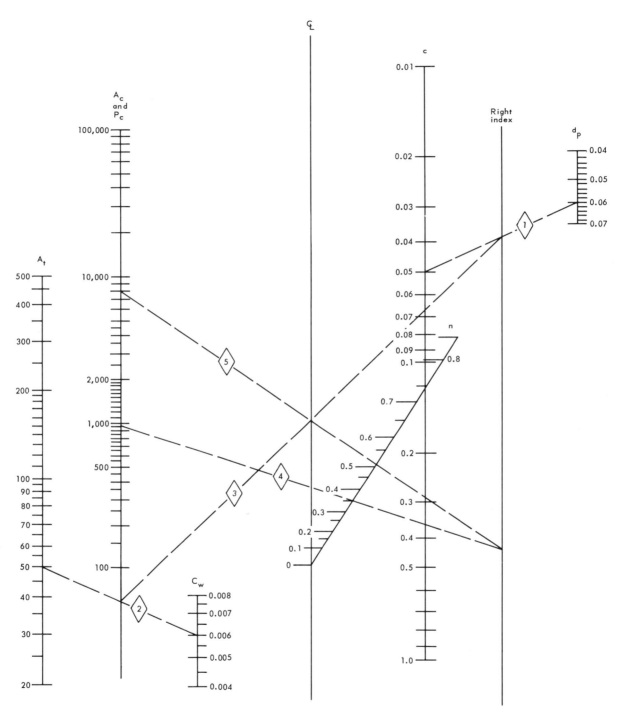

Fig. 6.6. Burning area pressure

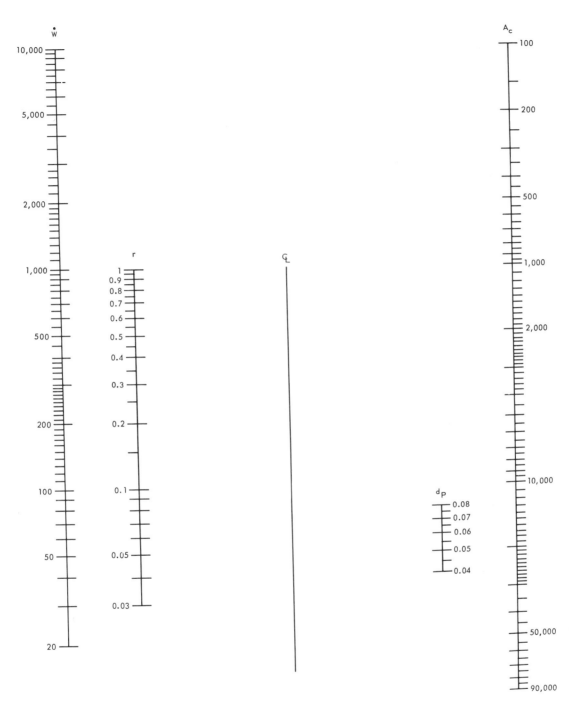

Fig. 6.7. Weight flow

TO USE: Select values of burning rate and propellant density and index centerline. Using this point as pivot, compare burning area values with corresponding weight flow values.

in terms of over-all impulse or vehicle acceleration. However, to achieve greater loading, either density must be increased (it usually ranges from 0.050 to 0.070 lb per cu in.) or the duct volume must be reduced.

Reducing the duct volume for a given duct length lessens the port or flow area, hence the port-to-throat area. When the throat area and the port area are equal, the sonic point may jump from the throat to the end of the grain. This can result in an increase in chamber pressure.

If the burning surface forward of some point along the grain produces a large enough weight flow and if the port or duct area at that point is small enough, sonic conditions may be present at that point. Variations of the burning rate, pressure, and port area result in the sonic condition's jumping from point to point within the grain. This causes unstable burning. Shock and/or extremely high pressure conditions may arise within the grain, possibly resulting in the malfunction of the rocket motor. Pressure conditions become independent of the throat area if the port area is less than the throat area.

If the duct is not tapered, the distance from the fore end to point x, at which sonic conditions might exist, can be defined as follows:

$$x = \frac{P_o A_p C_w}{2 r_o S d_p} \left[(\gamma + 1)/2 \right]^{[1/(\gamma - 1)]} \qquad (6\text{-}8)$$

where

s = perimeter
r_o = burning rate at fore end.

Therefore, wise design avoids port-to-throat area ratios of unity or less. General design can utilize a ratio of 2 and optimal design a ratio of 1.5.

Sliver

Tail off in an internally burning case-bonded grain, as shown in Fig. 6.8, results from the combustion of the propellant remaining after web burnout. Figure 7.24 in Chapter 7 shows the burning pattern of a six-point star. During combustion of the sliver, the chamber pressure falls rapidly; hence much of the sliver is burned inefficiently. Reduction of sliver is important in optimization (see also Figs. 7.25, 7.26, and 7.27).

Breakup

Externally burning grains, when the grain is reduced to a critical size by combustion, undergo a fragmentation that results in a pressure rise near burnout. If large fragments are present in small throats, clogging is apt to occur during discharge.

Grain stress

Stress deformation and/or cracking due to stress can cause malfunction of a solid propellant rocket. Stress deformations that

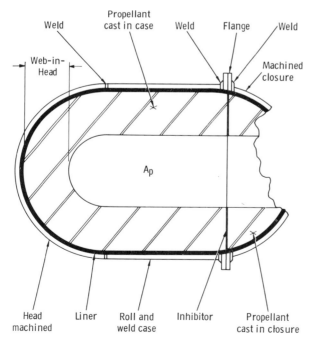

Fig. 6.8. Case-bonded design

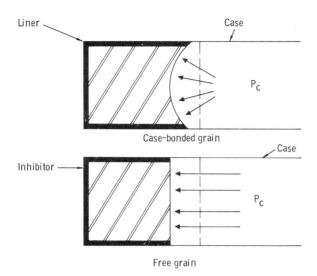

Fig. 6.9.   **End burning grains**

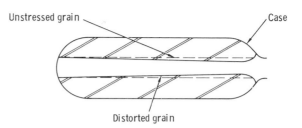

Fig. 6.10.   **Internal burning case-bonded grain**

of the grain tends to lessen the flow area and hence increase the difference between fore and aft pressures. The increase of this difference increases the deformation and produces a cycle that, under extreme conditions, may lead to excessive pressures and even closure of the flow area, resulting in malfunction of the motor. Obviously, if the propellant's elastic modulus is less than a critical value, the motor will blow up. This value may be determined by a study of the geometry, pressure parameters, and characteristics of the specific propellant.

Distortion of an internal burning case-bonded grain is illustrated in Fig. 6.10, whereas distortion of internal-external burning grain is illustrated in Fig. 6.11.

The stresses to be considered are:

1. Pressure difference
2. Acceleration
3. Gas flow drag.

These stresses are included in the following equation, where the subscript, g, represents the grain:

restrict the aft flow passage of a grain can cause a pressure rise that in turn amplifies the deformation. The result is a destructive cycle. Premature break-up of free-standing grains is often the result of grain stress. The exact geometry of the grain determines the stress complex.

The end burning grain is subject to longitudinal stress from chamber pressure and the acceleration of the rocket. Figure 6.9 illustrates the compressive action of the chamber pressure on a case-bonded grain and a free-standing inhibited grain. The stress formulation is

$$s = P_c + (a M_p / \pi R^2) \qquad (6\text{-}9)$$

where

P_c = chamber pressure
a = acceleration
M_p = mass
R = grain radius

Deformation of tubular and other grains subjected to differential pressure stresses can be serious. Three stressing conditions are present: (1) the difference between fore and aft pressures, (2) the acceleration effects, and (3) the gas flow drag. Distortion

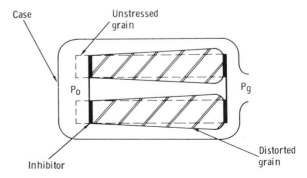

Fig. 6.11.   **Distortion of internal-external burning grain**

$$s = P_o - P_g + (aM_p/\text{propellant cross section})$$
$$+ \frac{fP_o^2 A_p (6r)^{-1}(bT)^{-1/2}(u^2/bT)_g^{1/2}}{\text{propellant cross section}} \quad (6\text{-}10)$$

where

f = friction coefficient
P_o = fore end pressure
u = gas velocity
b = specific gas constant
T = absolute temperature

The case-bonded internal burning grain in optimized design does not present areas for the fore and aft pressure difference to develop stresses. The grain is continuous to the fore end. Aft end pre-nozzle port areas are minimized. Thus basically, the stresses of a longitudinal nature to be considered are acceleration stresses and gas flow friction stresses. Hence, the $(P_o - P_g)$ term is eliminated in Eq. 6-10.

Internal burning grains are also subject to stress as a result of the chamber pressure. The maximum tensile stress for a thick-walled cylinder would be

$$s = P_c(R^2 + R_o^2)/(R^2 - R_o^2) \quad (6\text{-}11)$$

where

R = outer radius
R_o = inner radius.

Figure 6.12 illustrates these basic stress distribution equations. The inner maximum of the upper circular half follows the exact equation. For example, if P_c were 1,000 psi and R_o were equal to $\frac{1}{2} R$, the maximum stress would be 1,667 psi. The lower half at the centerline intersection where R_o is equal to zero would have a value equal to P_c, hence 1,000 psi. To evaluate stress distributions within the grain, the following two formulations express radial and tensile stress:

1. Radial:

$$s_r = P_c \Gamma R_o^2 \{1 - [R^2/(X^2 + Y^2)]\}/(R^2 - R_o^2) \quad (6\text{-}12)$$

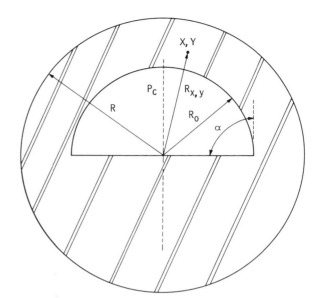

Fig. 6.12. Half-cylinder perforational stress concentration and distribution

2. Tensile:

$$s_t = P_c \Gamma R_o^2 \{1 + [R^2/(X^2 + Y^2)]\}/(R^2 - R_o^2) \quad (6\text{-}13)$$

where

$(X^2 + Y^2)$ = square of radius at point under consideration
Γ = stress concentration factor
$\Gamma^{-1} = (s_r' \pm s_t')/(s_r \pm s_t) \quad (6\text{-}14)$

where s' equals the stress without consideration of the concentration factor. (The plus-or-minus sign depends upon the direction of the point in reference to the center of grain.)

Figures 6.13 and 6.14 illustrate the stress concentration factor in terms of a hydraulic analogue. Stress may be interpreted in terms of velocity flow in a passage of infinite length or in a circular passage (as shown) with an infinite radius. Figure 6.14 diagrammatically shows the grain section as a hydraulic passage with clockwise flow illustrated as left to right flow.

Comparison of these two diagrams indicates that the velocity (stress) must be concentrated at point A, relieved at point B,

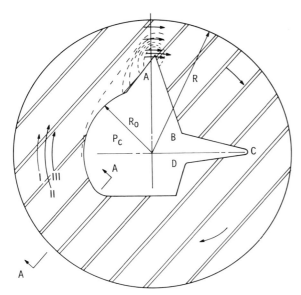

Fig. 6.13. Perforational stress concentration
I, II, and III indicate streamlines.

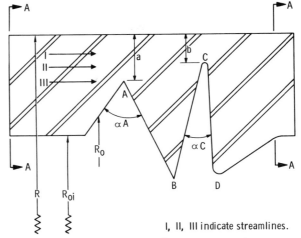

I, II, III indicate streamlines.

Fig. 6.14. Perforational stress concentration

concentrated at point C, and relieved at point D. Concentration at C will be increased by the fact that flow area "b" is smaller than flow area "a" (having closer streamlines) but lessened by the fact that the point radius is greater. In addition, the angle of attack—the angle affecting the flow stream—differs.

The formulation for the stress concentration factor is

$$\Gamma = 1 + (R_o/R_{o\max})^2 \times$$
$$\{[(K_s/R_1)(B' - R_{o\max})]^{0.33 \cos(0.5\,\alpha)} - 1\} \quad (6\text{-}15)$$

where

$R_{o\max}$ = maximum inner radius of projection

R_1 = projection point radius

K_s = stress constant

B' = distance to point B.

It follows directly that the minimum stress points B and D follow the formulation

$$\Gamma = 1 + [(R_{oi} - R_o)/(R_{oi} - R_{\min})]^2 \times$$
$$\{[(R_1/K_s)(R - R_{o\max})]^{0.33 \cos(0.5\alpha)} - 1\} \quad (6\text{-}16)$$

where R_{oi} = radius to surface i.

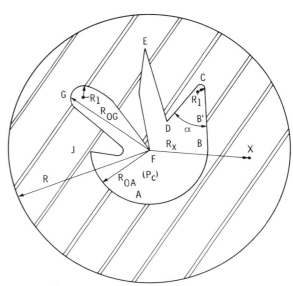

Fig. 6.15. General configuration stress concentration and distribution

For many propellants, K_s, equals about 5.3. Test of a specified propellant may reveal more exact design values.

Figure 6.15 illustrates a number of variations of inner contours. For maximum stress, which is often the value desired in the study, the following equation may be used:

$$s = \Gamma P_c(R^2 + R_o^2)/(R^2 - R_o^2) \quad (6\text{-}17)$$

This figure will be discussed by means of the following example. Consider a chamber pressure of 1,000 psi, a chamber radius, R,

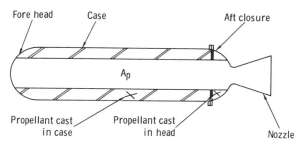

Fore head   Case   Aft closure

A_p

Propellant cast   Propellant cast
in case   in head   Nozzle

Fig. 6.16. Case-bonded configuration with propellant cast in aft closure

of 3 in., an R_o of 1 in. for the basic equivalent cylinder, and a range from 0.75 to 1.75. Considering the minimum point radius as 0.01 in., the concentration factors would be

$$\Gamma_{max} = 5.00$$
$$\Gamma_{min} = 0.34$$

Thus the equivalent cylinder stress would be 1,250 psi, but the actual maximum is five times 2,030, or 10,150 psi, at the outer star points whereas the minimum at the inner star points is only 384 psi. It is obvious that from the viewpoint of stress, outer points should be avoided in a perforation configuration.

Thermal stress of case-bonded grains

During storage, the grain undergoes a series of temperature changes. During temperature transition, stresses in the grain may be estimated directly from temperature gradients. However, the most severe stresses occur when thermal equilibrium is achieved. The maximum tensile stress occurs at the inner radius:

$$s_t = 2R^2 E(\Delta T)(\Delta\alpha)/[(1 - 2v)R^2 + r^2] \quad (6\text{-}18)$$

where

ΔT = change in temperature between points

$\Delta\alpha$ = difference between the coefficients of thermal expansion of grain and chamber

v = Poisson's ratio

E = modulus of elasticity of grain

r = inner radius of grain

R = chamber radius.

Case design

Case design is treated in detail in Chapter 17, but it must be considered in terms of the grain design and geometry. Weight considerations, operating pressures (chamber pressure), hence stress, and manufacturing methods must be considered during grain design. A center-joint case was shown in Fig. 6.5. This allows a highly loaded, internally burning grain but requires that the grain be joined at the centerline. Bonding of the propellant may lead to design problems. Figure 6.8 showed a case-bonded design with the head filled with propellant and joined to the main grain as in the center-joint design. The liner between the grain and case is shown. Figure 6.16 shows a typical case-bonded configuration with propellant cast in the aft closure. As weight considerations are paramount, the case weight should be minimized. Another type is the fiber-glass filament-wound case. In this instance, fiber glass is actually wound directly on the grain instead of a mandril to produce a low weight case.

7

Geometry

Grain geometry design is absolutely basic in solid rocket design. Final operation depends more on correct geometry than on any other function. Selection of the type of grain and of parametric relationships as expressed by geometry within the classification of grain selected posits specific advantages and disadvantages which the designer must consider.

Grains can be classified into four general types:

1. End-burning grain
2. External- and internal-burning grain
3. External-burning grain
4. Internal-burning grain.

The end-burning grain may be free-standing or case-bonded as the application warrants. The external-burning grains and the external- and internal-burning grains are free-standing. The internal-burning grain is usually case-bonded.

Burning area, pressure, and rate may increase with time (progressive burning curve), decrease as burning occurs (regressive curve), or remain the same throughout burning (neutral curve). Free-standing grain may burn externally and internally (see Fig. 7-1). In this case, the curve is neutral. Be-

cause the performance of a nonchanging burning curve remains constant, this grain is considered the ideal. Figure 7.2 illustrates an ideal internal-burning grain.

End-burning grains

Because the thrust of a rocket is proportional to the burning area of the grain, an end-burning design with constant burning area (see Fig. 7.3) has the distinct advantages of constant pressure and thrust without complications such as erosive burning. The burning face of an end-burning design does not suffer any erosive conditions. Resonance is minor and extremely transitory. Neither break-up nor sliver phenomena are present. However, serious limitations are present in that (1) the chamber wall is constantly exposed to combustion gases and (2) maximum pressures and burning areas are limited by the chamber radius.

The burning area is

$$A_c = \pi R^2 \qquad (7\text{-}1)$$

where R = chamber radius.

The web thickness equals the grain length. Hence, time of burn is

$$t_w = L_8/r \qquad (7\text{-}2)$$

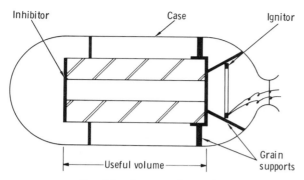

Fig. 7.1.   Free-standing grain

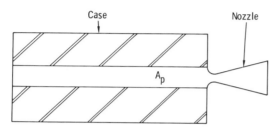

Fig. 7.2.   Ideal radial burning grain

With neutral burning perimeter, burning area remains constant.

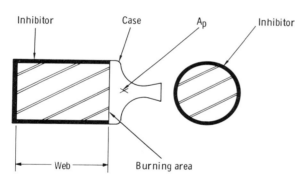

Fig. 7.3.   End burning design

where

$$L_g = \text{grain length}$$
$$r = \text{burning rate.}$$

The pressure remains constant, and the burning rate is also a constant for end-burning geometry (if variations of chamber radius are neglected). This simplifies a number of the basic equations. The burning rate exponent, n, effectively equals unity due to the lack of pressure variation. High loading (or weight efficiency) is possible. The web dis-

tance determines the useful volume and can be maximized.

The weight flow simplifies to

$$\dot{W} = r A_c d_p = K_w \qquad (7\text{-}3)$$

where d_p = solid propellant density.

Hence thrust becomes

$$F = K_w I_{sp} \qquad (7\text{-}4)$$

and chamber pressure becomes

$$P_c = K_w / A_t C_w \qquad (7\text{-}5)$$

where C_w = weight flow coefficient.

However, while the throat area is considered constant in preliminary design, throat erosion does take place (see Fig. 5-6.). If significant, this erosion leads to variations in chamber pressure and, consequently, burning rate, thrust, and weight flow, making the simplified equations invalid. In this case, the standard equations, without simplification, must be applied.

If, by multi-grain arrangement (see Fig. 7.4), dual-end burning is desired, a central gas passage must be provided as illustrated.

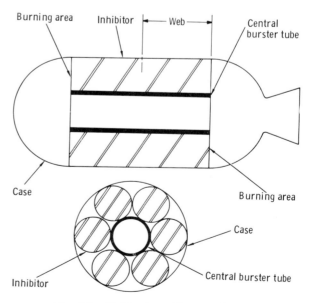

Fig. 7.4.   Multigrain end burning charge

Support of the grains becomes a major consideration in such grain arrangements.

Dual-burning increases the burning area (doubles it except for the gas passage area) but decreases time of burn to

$$t_w = L_8/2r \qquad (7\text{-}6)$$

The burning area (see Fig. 7.4) equals

$$A_c = 2\pi R_g^2 m \qquad (7\text{-}7)$$

where

R_g = radius of each grain
m = number of grains.

Exposure of the chamber walls for long periods results in thicker walls for end-burning grains. This heavy construction is illustrated in Fig. 6-9. The walls are thicker, in this case, to such a degree that plate heads are attached by flanges. Such a weight penalty severely limits over-all performance. Exposure of case walls also limits the flame temperature and, hence, specific impulse.

Thrust is limited by the maximum allowable radius. For example, a large-scale motor requiring 6,000 sq in. of burning area would require a motor diameter of about 89.5 in. This would be 1.8 times the diameter of a corresponding star perforation design.

End-burning grains are well suited to long-duration low thrust of a constant level as required for jet-assisted take-off units or auxiliary rockets for vector control of large-scale devices. They may be free-standing or case-bonded. Figure 6-10 shows the stress deformation of a case-bonded grain and a free-standing grain that utilizes the case for support. Stress characteristics are superior to other grains. Either method may be used.

Tubular grain

The tubular configuration (see Fig. 7.5) is an internal-external burning geometry. Tubular grains may be manufactured by

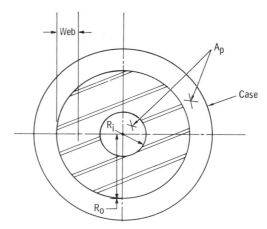

Fig. 7.5.   Tubular configuration

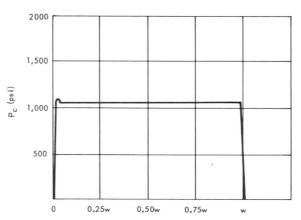

Fig. 7.6.   Tubular grain without ridges

casting or extrusion. Essentially a neutral burning configuration with basic simplicity of design, they are well suited to small-scale solid rocket motors. They can be inspected after manufacture so that faulty grains can be rejected prior to assembly.

A cylinder burning internally and externally with both ends inhibited will produce a neutral burning curve (see Fig. 7.6) with a constant burning area

$$A_c = 2\pi L_g (R_i + R_o) \qquad (7\text{-}8)$$

where

R_i = interior radius at any time of burn
R_o = corresponding outer radius.

The web thickness equals one-half the difference in initial radii. The time of burn is

$$t_w = w/r \qquad (7\text{-}9)$$

where w = web thickness.

The pressure remains constant, and the basic equations can be simplified. These simplified expressions for weight flow, thrust, and chamber pressure are identical in Equations 7-3, 7-4, and 7-5, respectively. If throat area variations due to erosion are significant, these simplified versions of the standard formulations cannot be utilized.

Propellant weight may be calculated by

$$W_p = L_g d_p (R_o^2 - R_i^2) \pi \qquad (7\text{-}10)$$

A tubular grain must be supported within the chamber in a manner that will provide flow area past the grain, as shown in Fig. 7.7. The fact that grain supports and case walls are subject to the environment of the hot combustion products must be considered.

Longitudinal support projections

One method of providing external flow area and grain support is by lengthwise projections (see Fig. 7.8) which will burn as determined by the uninhibited areas. Good design allows burning of the side only, thus retaining grain support for a greater dura-

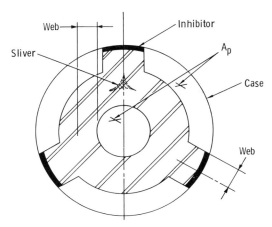

Fig. 7.8. **Tubular configuration with supporting ridges**

tion. Effective design and inhibiting can provide nearly neutral projection curve burn.

The equation for burning follows:

$$S = S_o + Brt \qquad (7\text{-}11)$$

where

S_o = initial burning perimeter

$$B = (2 W_p / w^2 L_g) - \frac{2\Delta A + S_o w}{w^2} \qquad (7\text{-}12)$$

$$\Delta A = 1.996 \, w^2 \qquad (7\text{-}13)$$

$$\text{Sliver} \, (Z_v) = 1.996 \, w^2 L_g \qquad (7\text{-}14)$$

$$A_c = S L_g \qquad (7\text{-}15)$$

Tubular grains are subject to both resonance and erosive phenomena. Resonance within the central burning region results in irregular peaks. Resonance burning can be reduced by use of either radial drill holes or a steel rod through the perforation, or by a combination of these as shown in Fig. 8.8.

Erosive burning converts a neutral to a progressive burn. Erosive conditions can be reduced by tapering the central duct area. The flow area is increased as the nozzle is approached, thus allowing greater duct area as mass flow increases and tending to neutralize erosive effects.

Tubular configurations are subject to maximum stress distortion as illustrated in

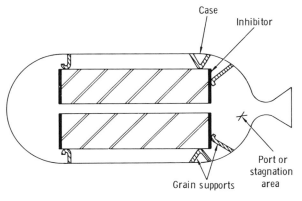

Fig. 7.7. **Radial burning grain**

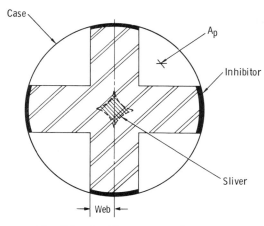

Fig. 7.9. Cruciform grain configuration

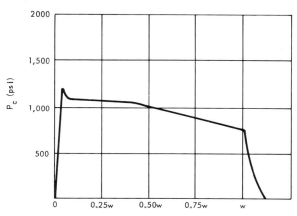

Fig. 7.10. Burning curve for helically inhibited cruciform grain

Fig. 6.12. Stress analysis of tubular grains is necessary since stresses can result in grain fracture and motor malfunction.

Cruciform

Like other external burning grains, the cruciform configuration can be manufactured and inspected prior to motor assembly (see Fig. 7.9). Thus grains with defects may be discarded before final assembly.

The loading of the motor is limited to the "useful volume" shown in Fig. 7.1. The cruciform configuration is resistant to both resonance and erosive burning.

The cruciform grain with correct inhibition presents a nearly neutral curve (see Fig.

7.10) with greater weight of propellant than possible with a tubular grain. The classical inhibition pattern is illustrated in Fig. 7.11. The burning area of the cruciform grain is

$$A_c = L_g S \qquad (7\text{-}16)$$

where

$$S = S_o + rt[(2\,W_p/w^2\,L_g\,d_p) - 1.7168 - 2\,S_o] \qquad (7\text{-}17)$$

$$\text{Sliver}\,(Z_v) = 0.8584\,w^2\,L_g \qquad (7\text{-}18)$$

Without inhibiting, the cruciform burning curve is regressive; with all peripheral surfaces inhibited, the curve is progressive. The degree of inhibition can provide the degree of regression, progression, or neutrality.

The cruciform grain is subject to stress deformation of the type illustrated in Fig. 6.12. Excessive distortion can result in blowup. This grain design is well suited for small-scale rocket motors. Like all external burning configurations, case walls are subjected to the hot combustion products with consequent flame temperature limits and/or material limitations.

The triform grain

The triform grain (see Fig. 7.12) has greater loading than either the tubular or the cruciform grains but also greater sliver or break-up potential near burnout. Grain

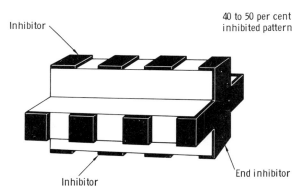

Fig. 7.11. Classical helical inhibition pattern for cruciform grain

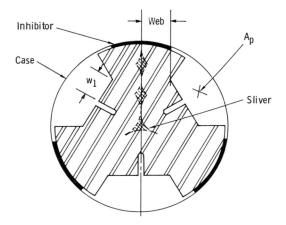

Fig. 7.12. Triform grain configuration

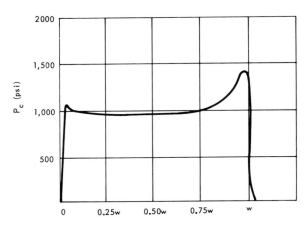

Fig. 7.13. Burning curve for triform grain

break-up is amplified by fore-to-aft pressure differentials. Like other non-case-bonded grains, the triform can be inspected after manufacture so that faulty grains can be rejected prior to assembly. The pressure curve is nearly neutral when inhibited for the full length of the grain, as shown in Fig. 7.13.

The design equations for triform grains follow:

From 0 to w_1 (see Fig. 7.12):

$$S = S_o + Brt \qquad (7\text{-}19)$$

From w_1 to w:

$$S = S_o + Bw_1 + 2\pi rt \qquad (7\text{-}20)$$

where

$$B = [(W_p/d_pL_g) - \Delta A - (w^2 - w_1^2) - S_o w]$$
$$\div [ww_1 - (w_1^2/2)] \qquad (7\text{-}21)$$

$$\Delta A = w^2 \{0.152 - 6\sin^{-1}[w_1(w^2 - w_1^2)^{1/2}]$$
$$+ 12 w_1/(w^2 - w_1^2)^{1/2}\}$$
$$+ 12 w_1[w - (w^2 - w_1^2)^{1/2}] \qquad (7\text{-}22)$$

$$A_c = L_g S \qquad (7\text{-}23)$$

$$\text{Sliver}\ (Z_v) = L_g \Delta A \qquad (7\text{-}24)$$

Loading is limited to the useful volume of the chamber as illustrated in Fig. 7.1. Cross-sectional loading is high. This geom-etry is not subject to significant erosion or resonance. However, maximum feasible grain diameters restrict use to small-scale rocket motors. Although near-burnout structure is better than cruciform, the increase in sliver provides a greater break-up peak. The case must be designed for a hot gas environment as with other exterior burning grains.

Hexaform and octaform

The hexaform, six-armed configuration shown in Fig. 7.14 and the octaform, eight-armed version of this configuration are both designed for extrusion manufacture. This

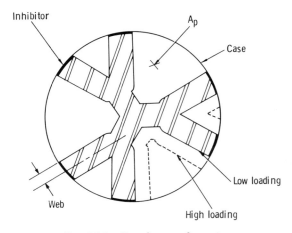

Fig. 7.14. Hexaform configuration

figure shows a small web thickness, hence light loading. The dotted line section indicates heavy loading with increased web. Thus a heavy loading has increased unburned residue. The increase in central sliver is proportional to the square of the web. Naturally, loading is restricted to the "useful volume" of the chamber as illustrated in Fig. 7.1.

The formula for the hexaform and octaform grain is

$$S = S_o + Brt \qquad (7-25)$$

where, for the hexaform

$$B = 2w^{-2}[(W_p/d_pL_g) - 0.152w^2 - S_ow] \qquad (7-26)$$

and for the octaform

$$B = 2w^{-2}[(W_p/d_pL_g) - 0.8584w^2 - S_ow \qquad (7-27)$$

$$A_c = SL_g \qquad (7-28)$$

These grains are not subject to erosion or resonance. Faults in the grain may be discovered prior to assembly. Break-up characteristics are superior to those for tubular grains. The burning curve is regressive as shown in Fig. 7.15.

Grains of this general configuration are subject to distortion of the type illustrated in Fig. 6.12 as the result of the difference between fore-and-aft pressures. As with all external burning grains, the case walls are exposed to hot combustion products.

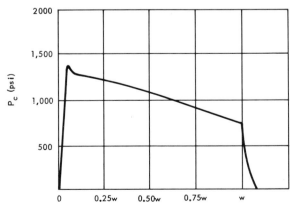

Fig. 7.15. Burning curve for hexaform grain

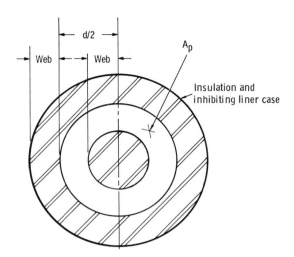

Fig. 7.16. Rod and cylinder configuration

Rod and cylinder

The rod and cylinder configuration (see Fig. 7.16) presents an ideal geometry with a neutral curve which may be either freestanding or case-bonded. However, difficulties in rod support limit its use. Supports for the central rod must be exposed to the combustion products, but case-bonding of the cylinder protects the case from the hot gases. Upper flame temperature limits are partially established by the heat resistance of inert parts. When loading is high, this geometry is subject to erosive burning.

Break-up can be reduced by use of two propellants, one for the cylinder and another for the rod. With a smaller rod web and slower burning rate, the structural continuity of the rod is retained longer. Percentage of chamber used and grain stress characteristics depend on design utilization. Use of fore-and-aft areas is restricted by rod support requirements.

The design equations follow:

$$S = 2\pi[w + (d/2)] \qquad (7-29)$$

$$A_c = SL_g \qquad (7-30)$$

Slab

The slab configuration (see Fig. 7.17) is easy to manufacture by extrusion or casting.

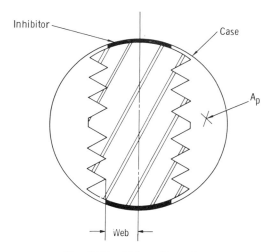

Fig. 7.17.   Slab configuration

Flaws may be detected before assembly of the rocket motor. This design minimizes burning area while maximizing duration and weight loading. Although initial burning area cannot be changed greatly, variation of the surface contours allows selection of correct burning area at initiation. However, after the initial burning surface contours have burned through (past w_1), the surface assumes a slightly progressive curve of standard cross section.

The equations for the slab follow:

From 0 to w_1:

$$S = S_o + Brt \qquad (7\text{-}31)$$

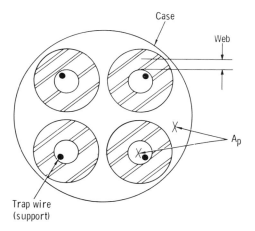

Fig. 7.18.   Multitubular grains supported by trap wire

From w_1 to w:

$$S = (S_o + Bw_1) \times$$
$$\left[1 + \frac{\{R - [R^2 - (w - w_1)^2]^{1/2}\}(rt - w_1)}{(w - w_1)[R^2 - (w - w_1)^2]^{1/2}} \right]$$
$$(7\text{-}32)$$

where

$$B = [(W_p/d_p L_g) - \Delta A - S_o w]/(w w_1 - 0.5 w_1^2)$$
$$(7\text{-}33)$$

Both w_1 and ΔA must be determined by face geometry of the specific slab grain. Case walls are exposed to combustion products and thus require heavier construction than case-bonded designs. Erosion characteristics are minimized, and resonance does not seem to affect the pressure curve.

Multi-grains

Multi-grain configurations provide a method of constructing medium-sized rocket motors from small grains. Extrusion grains can be used without retooling and use of larger equipment.

Figure 7.18 illustrates tubular grains supported by trap wires. These wires, incidentally, reduce resonance conditions in the same manner as a resonance rod. Maximum loading consists of the four-unit multi-grain. Larger configurations utilizing more grains present lower loadings.

Figure 7.4 showed end-burning grains with a central burster tube. Multi-grain design follows the same formulations as the single grain but amplifies the inherent defects. Loading is minimized, and break-up is maximized. Increased support results in increased inert weight.

Conical cylinder

The conical-cylinder grain (see Fig. 7.19) is an optimal three-dimensional geometry. Case-bonding protects the walls from the hot combustion products until web burn-

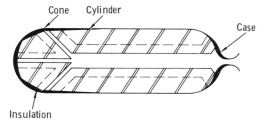

Fig. 7.19.   Conical cylinder grain

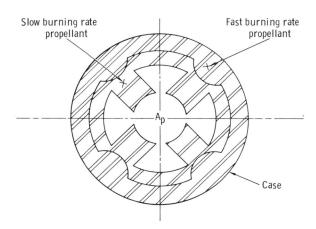

Fig. 7.20.   Four-point dual propellant grain

out. The case requires insulation in exposed areas, and, to a lesser degree, in areas to be exposed during part of the combustion cycle. This configuration is subject to erosive burning; otherwise the grain would have no sliver or pressure tail-off. However, the fore end tends to burn out after the aft end due to the increase in burning rate as a result of erosive burning maximized at the aft end. Resonance peaks are apt to appear in the pressure curves in this type of grain during the first third of burn.

The equations for the conical cylinder grain follow:

$$\text{Effective } S = A_c/L_g \qquad (7\text{-}34)$$

$$A_c = A_{co} + 2\pi Lrt + (rt\,BA_{co}/L) + 2\pi B(rt)^2 \qquad (7\text{-}35)$$

where

A_{co} = initial burning area
L = effective grain length

$$B = \frac{[(W_p/d_p) - wA_{co} - Lw^2]}{[(w^2A_{co}/2L_g) + (2\pi w^3/3)]} \qquad (7\text{-}36)$$

Duct area closure may result from stress conditions as illustrated in Fig. 6.12.

Manufacturing can be simplified by casting the cone in the fore head and casting the cylinder separately. However, meltable cores allow casting within a one-unit case.

Dual propellant grains

Booster and sustainer may be cast as a single grain by casting a second grain in conjunction with the first. The grain in Fig. 7.20 (its pressure curve is shown in Fig. 7.21) was designed to minimize tail-off, and not for booster-sustainer purposes. In this design, slow-burning propellant is consumed first, then fast-burning propellant equalizes the curve. For a booster-sustainer motor, fast-burning propellant is utilized first, then a slow-burning propellant to sustain the thrust.

Case-bonding

Development of the large-scale solid rocket motor was based on the case-bonding

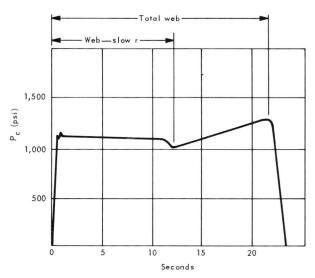

Fig. 7.21.   Pressure curve for dual propellant grain

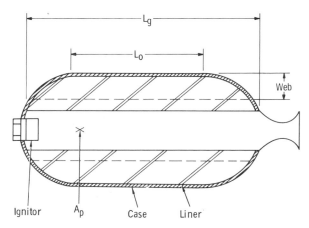

Fig. 7.22.   Interior burning case-bonded grain

core used to cast the proper perforation configuration), the propellant and liner are cured or otherwise set. After the core has been removed, the grain resembles that illustrated in Fig. 7.22. An additional application of insulation may be used where sections of the case are exposed. Where possible, propellant should be used to provide protection. For example, web in the fore head will protect the fore end of the case. When passage through the web is necessary, the exposure can be minimized by good design.

of elasticized propellants. Case-bonding (see Fig. 7.22) eliminates internal supports and protects chamber walls from the combustion products. The wall could therefore be lightened without experiencing the adverse effects of heat.

Compactness, simplicity, and reliability are hallmarks of case-bonded motors. Elasticized propellants reduce the danger of cracking and the resultant lack of performance predictability. Case-bonding is accomplished by lining the case with an inhibiting insulating and bonding material, then pouring in the propellant. Figure 7.23 shows the basic configuration. After the application of the liner to the inner walls of the case and the filling with propellant (with a

Star

The basic star configuration allows variation of initial perimeter, hence of burning area, for a constant length of grain. The combustion progress of a six-point star is illustrated in Fig. 7.24. Successive surface configurations are shown clockwise, numbered I to V. Section I shows the initial surface. Section II shows the progress of the burn normal to all surfaces. The arc tip increases as a semi-circle. The projection

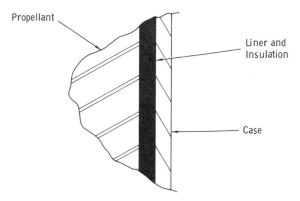

Fig. 7.23.   Case bonding detail

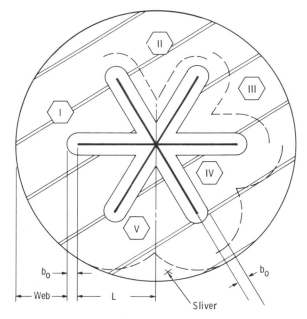

Fig. 7.24.   Combustion development of star

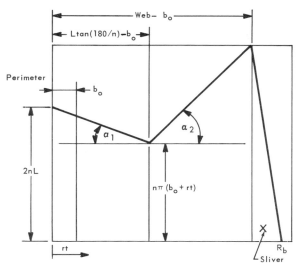

Fig. 7.25. Combustion development of star (perimeter—distance burned)

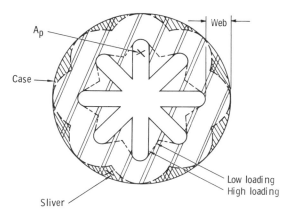

Fig. 7.26. Eight-point star

sides move out parallel to the centerline of the star point. Section III shows the approach to cusp formation. Section IV shows the instant of cusp formation. Section V depicts the burn to the point of sliver formation and web burn-out. The heavy centerlines indicate the reduced star, which is the basic configuration. At an effective burned distance, b_o, equal to the half width of the star point, we obtain the illustrated star at initial conditions. (The reduced star would have zero duct area. It is the simple set of projection centerlines—a star with zero arm thickness, that is, $b_o = 0$.)

The reduced star method allows description of stars in terms of families of n pointed stars, with side length L as shown in Fig. 7.25. Use of these relationships, for optimal star configurations, can provide perimeter values throughout burn. Reduction of b_o and a relative increase in L to keep web constant increase optimization potential. Figure 7.26 illustrates an eight-point star.

The dotted lines indicate the standard method for reducing burning area, increasing duct area, and lowering weight of propellant with a given web. Variations of b_o, L, duct area, and perimeter must be made to determine the best configuration for the specific design.

The general equations for stars follow:

From 0 to w_1:

$$S = S_o + rtB \qquad (7\text{-}37)$$

From w_1 to w:

$$S = S_o + Bw_1 + 2\pi rt \qquad (7\text{-}38)$$

where

$$B = \frac{(R^2 - A_{po} - wS_o - \pi w^2 + \pi w_1^2 - \Delta A)}{(ww_1 - 0.5\,w_1^2)}$$

$$(7\text{-}39)$$

$$w_1 = L \tan(\pi/m) - b_o \qquad (7\text{-}40)$$

and ΔA is defined by Eq. 7-41 at the bottom of the page.

$$\text{Sliver}\,(Z_v) = L_o \Delta A \qquad (7\text{-}42)$$

where L_o = final grain length.

$$\Delta A = \pi R^2 - (w + b_o)^2 \{\pi + m \sin^{-1}[L \sin(\pi/m)/(w + b_o)]\}$$

$$-mL^2 \sin(\pi/m)\{1 - [L^2 \sin^2(0.5\pi/m)/(w + b_o)^2]\}^{1/2} - mL^3[\sin(\pi/m)\cos(\pi/m)]/wb \qquad (7\text{-}41)$$

where m = the number of points

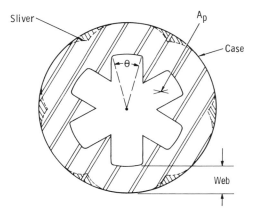

Fig. 7.27. Six-point star with fillet angle

$$A_c = L_e S \qquad (7\text{-}43)$$

where L_e = effective grain length.

The introduction of a "fillet angle" as illustrated in Fig. 7.27 reduces sliver. However, introduction of this angle reduces potential loading. Comparison of advantages and disadvantages must be made in reference to specific design.

Star configurations are subject to erosive burning, but resonance is minimized.

Equations for stars with fillet angles follow:

From 0 to w_1

$$S = S_o + rtB \qquad (7\text{-}44)$$

From w_1 to w:

$$S = S_o + Bw_1 + 2\pi rt \qquad (7\text{-}45)$$

where

$$B = (R^2 - A_{po} - wS_o + w_1{}^2 - w^2 - \Delta A) \div (ww_1 - 0.5 w_1{}^2) \qquad (7\text{-}46)$$

$$w_1 = L \tan [(\pi/m) - \theta] - b_o \qquad (7\text{-}47)$$

where θ is angle shown in Fig. 7.27 and ΔA is defined by Eq. 7-48 at the bottom of this page.

$$\text{Sliver} (Z_v) = L_o \Delta A \qquad (7\text{-}49)$$

$$A_c = L_e S \qquad (7\text{-}50)$$

For preliminary studies, the burning curve slope may be determined from Fig. 7.28 and the range of allowable burning area from Fig. 7.29.

The wagonwheel

The wagonwheel is an extension of the star pattern. Figure 7.30 illustrates the basic wagonwheel. Use of the fillet angle is paramount. Figure 7.31 shows a highly loaded version. When length of the spokes vary, computations must include this variation. Wagonwheels, when heavily loaded, are subject to high erosion characteristics and when lightly loaded tend to exhibit resonance.

Using the definitions illustrated in Fig. 7.32, the formula for the wagon wheel is:
From 0 to w_1:

$$S = S_o + (rt/w_1)(\Sigma_o - S_o) \qquad (7\text{-}51)$$

From w_1 to w:

$$S = \Sigma_1 + rtB \qquad (7\text{-}52)$$

From 0 to w when $w_1 = w$

$$S = (rt/w)(\Sigma_2 - S_o) + S_o \qquad (7\text{-}53)$$

where B, ΔA, Σ_0, Σ_1, and Σ_2 are defined by Eqs. 7-54 through 7-58 displayed at the bottom of page 77.

$$\Delta A = R^2 - A_{po} - 0.5\theta R^2 + 0.5\theta(L + b_o)^2 - (w + b_o)^2 \left\{ \pi + m \sin^{-1} \left[\frac{L \sin [(\pi/m) - 0.5\theta]}{w + b_o} \right] \right\}$$

$$- mL^2 \left\{ 1 - \left[\frac{L^2 \sin^2 [(\pi/m) - 0.5\theta]}{(w + b_o)^2} \right] \right\}^{1/2} \sin [(\pi/m) - 0.5\theta]$$

$$- mL^3 (w + b_o)^{-1} \sin [(\pi/m) - 0.5\theta] \cos [(\pi/m) - 0.5\theta] \qquad (7\text{-}48)$$

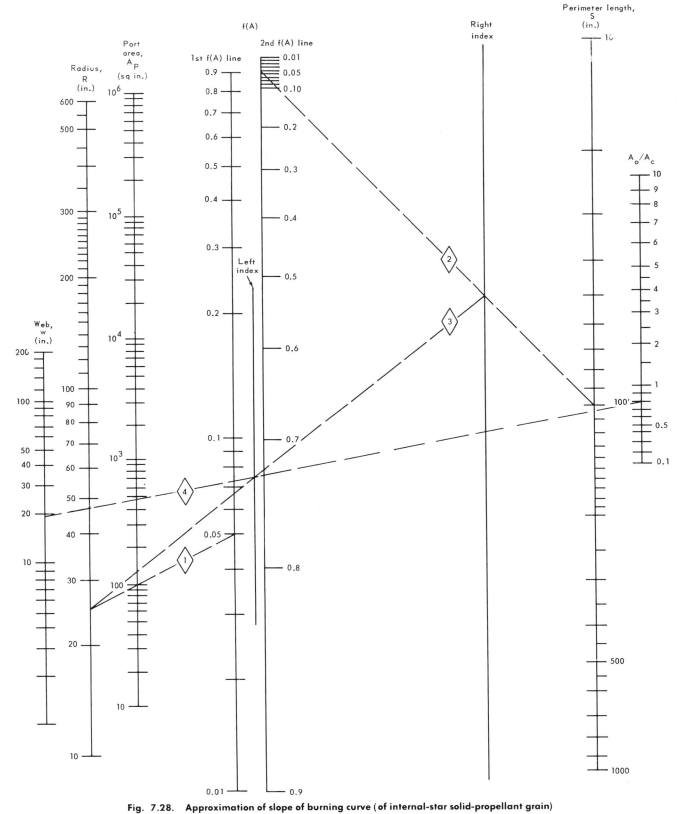

Fig. 7.28. Approximation of slope of burning curve (of internal-star solid-propellant grain)

TO USE: (1) Connect port area and radius to intersect a value of f(A) on first line and transfer to second f(A) line. (2) Connect this value with perimeter line to intersect point on right index. (3) Connect point on right index with radius to intersect left index. (4) Using this point, connect web value to intersect ratio of final burning area to initial burning area on right line.

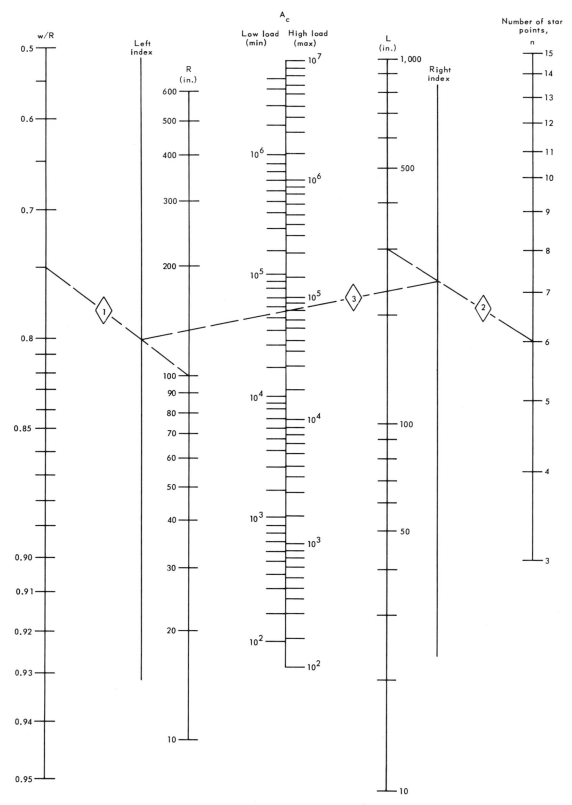

Fig. 7.29. Range of burning area allowable in preliminary design

For estimating the range of burning area for a given set of physical parameters of an internal burning star configuration solid-propellant grain. Minimum and maximum areas are estimated via center index.

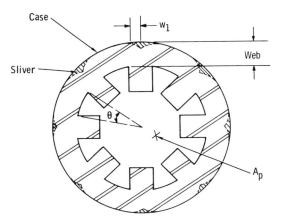

Fig. 7.30. Wagonwheel with eight points

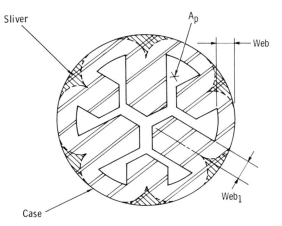

Fig. 7.31. Wagonwheel with six points

$$\text{Sliver } (Z_v) = L_o \Delta A \qquad (7\text{-}59)$$

$$A_c = SL_e \qquad (7\text{-}60)$$

$$\text{Sliver } = \Delta A L_o \qquad (7\text{-}63)$$

$$A_c = SL_e \qquad (7\text{-}64)$$

The anchor

The anchor (Fig. 7.33) has high weight efficiency but limited perimeter variation characteristics. Its major advantage is minimizing sliver and tail-off. The case is protected by the propellant to a maximum degree. This grain is subject to erosive burning.

A formula for the anchor (with $w = w_1$) follows:

$$S = S_o + (rt/w^2)[2(\pi R^2 - A_{po} - \Delta A - wS_o)] \qquad (7\text{-}61)$$

where

$$\Delta A = 1.047R^2 - 5.56(w + b_1)^2 \qquad (7\text{-}62)$$

Effective grain length

An interior burning grain of the type illustrated in Fig. 7.22 effectively changes length during burn from grain length to cylinder length. Thus the burning tends to give a regressive curve.

The effective length for ellipsoidal and semi-spherical headed grains follows this formula:

$$L_e = L_o + (L_g - L_o)(2Rw - w^2)^{-1/2} \times$$
$$[2R(w - rt) - (w - rt)^2]^{1/2} \qquad (7\text{-}65)$$

where

L_e = effective grain length
L_g = grain length

$$B = 2(w^2 - w_1^2)^{-1}[\pi R^2 - A_{po} - \Delta A + 0.5w_1(\Sigma_o - S_o) - w\Sigma_o] \qquad (7\text{-}54)$$

$$\Delta A = \pi R^2 - \theta m R^2 - mR^2 \sin^{-1}\{(w/R)\sin[(\pi/m) - 0.5\theta]\} + mww_1 \qquad (7\text{-}55)$$

$$\Sigma_o = m\left\{L_1 + L_2 - 2w - w\theta + R\theta + w_1\left[\pi + \theta + 2\left(\tan\alpha - \frac{1 - \tan 0.5\alpha}{1 + \tan 0.5\alpha}\right)\right]\right\} \qquad (7\text{-}56)$$

$$\Sigma_1 = \pi w_1(m + 2) + m\theta(R - w - w_1) \qquad (7\text{-}57)$$

$$\Sigma_2 = m\left[L_1 + L_2 + 1.14w + R\theta - 2\tan\alpha + \frac{2 - 2\tan 0.5\alpha}{1 + \tan 0.5\alpha}\right] \qquad (7\text{-}58)$$

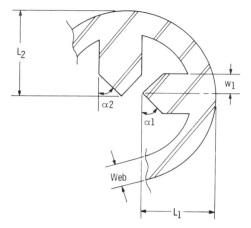

Fig. 7.32. Wagonwheel

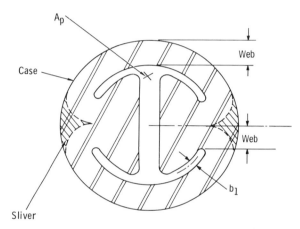

Fig. 7.33. Anchor

L_o = cylinder length.

A progressive perforation perimeter curve coupled with the above regressive effective length curve can produce an over-all neutral curve where

$$A_c = SL_e \qquad (7\text{-}66)$$

Segmented motors

Large-scale motors, in excess of 70 in. in diameter, can be manufactured in segments like building blocks (Fig. 7.34) and assembled on the launching site. While segmentation provides variable total stage impulse by addition or subtraction of segments and provides a reasonable method of trans-

Fig. 7.34. One of three center chamber segments of solid propellant rocket motor

portation of segments to the site, a weight penalty is suffered due to the need for flanges or other means of joining the segment cases (see Fig. 7.35). For a two-million-pound thrust motor, the segmented motor's inert parts would weigh about one-half more than the mono-grain.

Due to the increase in components, reliability would decrease. A motor with a reliability of 0.99 per cent for a single grain would have a reliability of .955 per cent if cast in five segments. However, the ability to inspect and reject defective segments would tend to increase this reliability figure.

Segments may be of a standard cylindrical shape or tapered to provide a truncated conical configuration. Tapered port areas in either configuration would reduce erosive burning conditions, which could be extreme in such high mass flow motors.

Spherical grain

The concept of the spherical motor (Fig. 7.36) has long been of interest since it

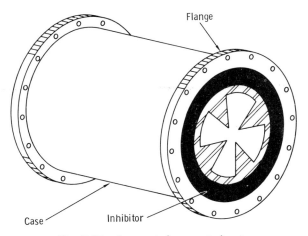

Fig. 7.35. Segment of segmented motor

would provide a lightweight motor because of the superior stress characteristics of a sphere. However, geometry of a spherical grain is difficult because of two basic considerations: (1) A three-dimensional grain is hard to visualize and difficult to neutralize; complex interior shapes, such as three-dimensional star configurations, are apt to be subject to port area variations greater than the basic star; and (2) the need for an interior burning configuration leads to difficulties in extracting cores during the manufacture of these configurations. Even the use of meltable cores has inherent limitations in drainability.

The design in Fig. 7.36 follows the formulation,

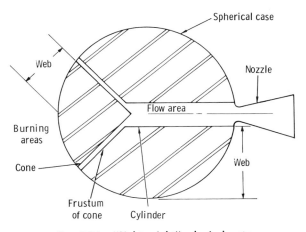

Fig. 7.36. "Lightweight" spherical motor

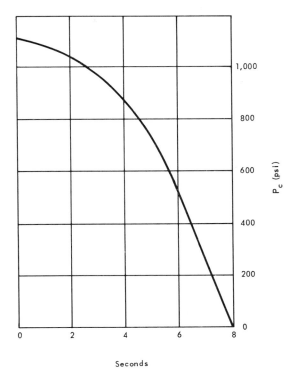

Fig. 7.37. "Lightweight" spherical motor pressure/time curve

$$A_c = A_{co} + B_1(rt) + B_2(rt)^2 \qquad (7\text{-}67)$$

Values of B_1 and B_2 depend upon the conic parameters and port areas of the specific grain. Three-dimensional stars, wagon-wheels, and other standard perforations obey the same spherical grain formulation with variations only in B_1 and B_2 values if w equals w_1.

Figure 7.37 shows a typical regressive pressure–time curve for this type of motor.

Tunnels, drills, or radial holes

Figure 7.38 illustrates the additional increases of burning area introduced by a hole in the grain normal to the burning surface. Such drills may be utilized for a number of purposes, including reduction of resonance gas passages and tunnels. These are classified into two types: (1) Drills connecting two burning surfaces, and (2) drills from one burning surface either dead-ended or leading to restricted surface.

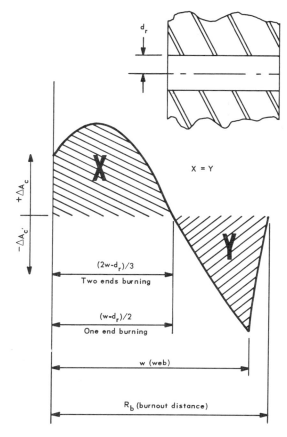

Fig. 7.38. Added area due to burn and inclusion of tunnels, drills, or radial holes

The approximation formulations expressing the addition to the burning surface are the following:

Two burning ends:

$$\Delta A = 4\pi d_r w - 2\pi d_r^2 + 4\pi rt(w - 2d_r)$$
$$- 6\pi(rt)^2 \qquad (7\text{-}68)$$

where d_r = drill radius.

One burning end:

$$\Delta A = 2\pi d_r w - 2\pi d_r^2 + 2\pi rt(w - 3d_r)$$
$$- 4\pi(rt)^2 \qquad (7\text{-}69)$$

Examination of Fig. 7.38 reveals that the added area due to introduction of the drill becomes negative after a specific burning distance: $(2w - d_r)/3$ for the dual-end burning and $(w - d_r)/2$ for the single-end burning. It should be noted that the area bounded by the positive curve must be exactly equal to the area bounded by the negative curve. Computations of performance are often in error by considering only the right side of the curve.

Duct areas

Flow areas of perforational configurations may be estimated by the general equations:
From 0 to w_1:

$$A_p = A_{po} + rt\,B + \pi(rt)^2 \qquad (7\text{-}70)$$

From w_1 to w:

$$A_p = A_{po} + Bw_1 + \pi[w_1^2 + (rt)^2]$$
$$+ 2rt(\pi)^{1/2}(A_{po} + Bw_1 + \pi w_1^2)^{1/2} \quad (7\text{-}71)$$

where

$$B = \left[\frac{w2(\pi)^{1/2}}{w_1}\right]^{1/2}(2w^2 - \pi R^2 + \Delta A)^{1/2}$$
$$- \pi w_1 - (A_{po} - \pi R^2 + \Delta A + 3\pi w^2)/w_1$$
$$(7\text{-}72)$$

Tapered duct areas may be estimated by using mean initial flow areas.

Thrust termination for solid propellants

Range may be accurately controlled by exact termination of thrust on command. By exact termination, exact velocity can be determined. For ballistics and for space trajectories, such control of thrust is desired on command. With propellants exhibiting a comparatively high minimum combustion pressure, termination may be accomplished by a sudden expansion of the exhaust area. However, methods of termination by a sudden cessation of pressure are often subject to chuffing and erratic termination.

A better method involves the use of thrust neutralization by vector-opposition ports. Usually blow-out ports on the fore head are utilized. These ports have an area sufficient to balance thrust exactly. However, if a passage to the blow-out port is not present during the early phases of burn, termination may not be accomplished until a gas passage is formed.

A passage to each port varies the geometry, hence may or may not be desirable in a specific design. Side blow-out ports, direct-ing the gases forward for vector neutraliza-tion and leading directly from the pre-nozzle port area, allow termination at any point of burn.

Use of side blow-out ports should be studied in terms of specific design and aero-dynamics. Side ports used with a heat con-ductive case can lead to blow-up prior to total thrust termination.

8

Burning Rates and Ignition

The linear burning rate of a solid propellant is the rate (usually in inches per second) at which the propellant is consumed normal to its burning surface as specified by the standard formulation:

$$r = c P_c^n \qquad (8\text{-}1)$$

The coefficient, c, represents the burning rate at 1,000 psi divided by 1,000 psi to the exponential constant, n:

$$c = r \text{ at } 1{,}000 \text{ psi}/(1{,}000)^n \qquad (8\text{-}2)$$

This assumes that the burning rate obeys the following ratio:

$$r/r_x = P^n/P_x^n \qquad (8\text{-}3)$$

where the optional burning-rate pressure parameter, x, was selected at a 1,000-psi, experimentally determined reference rate.

Hence, for a given propellant, a basic value of $r_{(1,000)}$ can be determined by test at 1,000 psi. The value of the exponent, n, can be determined statistically at other pressures.

Figure 8.1 relates burning rates graphically, and Fig. 8.2 compares burning rate exponents. Exact knowledge of the values of c and n can be obtained only by a large number of Strand burner tests of the specific batch to be used. Variations exist from batch to batch. However, these relatively precise values are suitable for design in that reproducibility is usually within 1 per cent.

The design nomograph, Fig. 8.6, allows rapid evaluation of burning rates. Changes of pressure during operation can be accounted for readily from the graph.

Temperature sensitivity

The sensitivity of the burning rate to the propellant temperature may be expressed in terms of an experimentally determined base reference temperature, T_r. This can be interpreted as a function of the oxidizer and can be assumed to affect only the constant c in the burning rate equation, which can be rewritten

$$r = c P_c^n/(T_r - T_p) \qquad (8\text{-}4)$$

where T_p is the propellant temperature, and the value of T_r should approximate 550°F ($\pm 50°$) for ammonium perchlorate or ammonium nitrate oxidizer propellants, 500°F($\pm 100°$) for double-base propellants, and be, in excess of 700°F for potassium perchlorate oxidizer propellants.

Fig. 8.3 shows the effects of propellant temperature on a pressure firing curve. Higher temperatures increase the burning rate; lower temperatures lower the burning rate. For grains in a transient temperature state, temperature gradients must be established through the grain to determine variations of burning rate.

An alternate expression for temperature sensitivity is

$$r = c[e^{k(T_r - T_p)}]P_c^n \qquad (8\text{-}5)$$

where

e = natural log base
k = experimental constant.

Selection of the correct formulation to express the temperature will depend upon experimental data. Either may serve for initial design.

Autoignition temperature

The reference temperature, T_r, has been found to differ from the autoignition temperature. For exact autoignition values, tests of specific propellant batches must be obtained; but T_r provides an order-of-magnitude value. It may be used as an approximation, but one must remember that autoignition often occurs at temperatures below this figure.

Autoignition varies with environmental conditioning, such as time of exposure, storage conditions, and size and configuration of grain. All data must be analyzed in considering autoignition. Chemical changes during storage can influence it. Great care should be used in interpreting the reference temperature in terms of ignition values. It should be noted, however, that an estimated autoignition temperature (with large tolerance

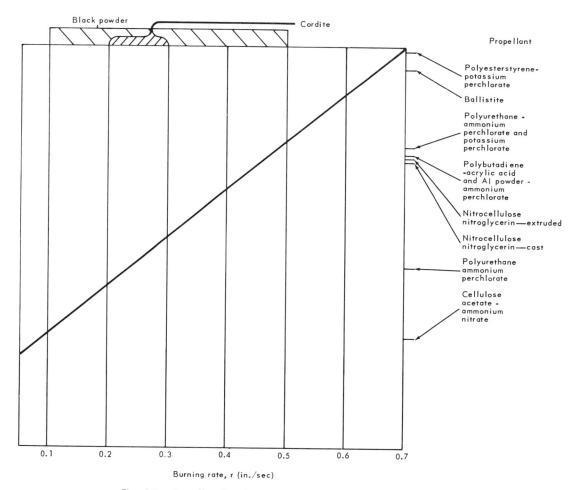

Fig. 8.1. Propellant burning rates at 1,000-psi chamber pressure, 60°F

allowed) is apt to be more valid in design than an exact value from a series of tests that are completely valid only for the tested propellant batch. The ignition temperature must be estimated within reasonable limits, for the specific propellant to be used, to ensure safe storage and design reliability.

Temperature limits

Propellants display individual temperature limits. Many will not function properly at elevated temperatures. Some will have faulty combustion characteristics at temperatures above 150°F; others have greater tolerances. At very low temperatures, faulty ignition and erratic combustion, in addition to poor physical properties, are characteristic of some propellants. Temperature limits for a given solid propellant must be established by tests.

Erosive burning

Propellant gases, when sweeping past a burning surface, tend to increase the burning

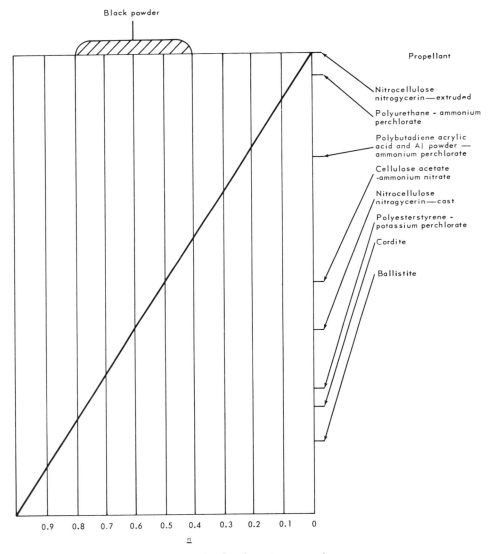

Fig. 8.2.   Burning rate exponents

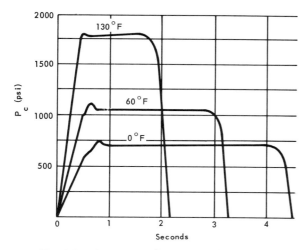

Fig. 8.3. **Temperature-burning rate dependency**

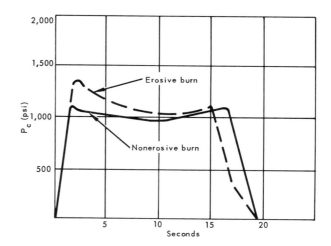

Fig. 8.5. **Erosive burning in five-point star**

rate of the surface by removing the insulating layer of combustion gas products. This increase has been determined experimentally to be in direct ratio to mass flow. The increase in initial burning rate and corresponding pressure rise is illustrated in Fig. 8.4. It may be noted that the ignition peak is amplified. Often this amplification leads to confusion when interpreting the curve in terms of too high an erosion coefficient in erosion studies. The correct erosion prediction curve will match the main body of the curve, but the ignition peak will continue to interrupt formulated prediction.

While burnout will occur at the same predicted time, the web begins to burn out

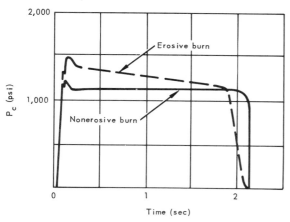

Fig. 8.4. **Regressive burn due to erosive effect on neutral tubular grain**

at the aft end prior to the fore end. This produces a tail-off effect in a sliverless grain.

$$r_e = r[1 + K_e(\dot{W}/\dot{W}_r)] \qquad (8\text{-}6)$$

where the flow ratio

$$\dot{W}/\dot{W}_r = 2\dot{W}(P_o A_p C_w)^{-1}[2/(\gamma - 1)]^{[1/(\gamma-1)]} \qquad (8\text{-}7)$$

Hence

$$r_e = r\{1 + 2\dot{W}K_e(P_o A_p C_w)^{-1}[2/(\gamma - 1)]^{[1/(\gamma-1)]}\}$$
$$(8\text{-}8)$$

where

$$
\begin{aligned}
r_e &= \text{erosive burning rate} \\
r &= \text{burning rate without erosion} \\
K_e &= \text{erosive constant discussed below} \\
\dot{W} &= \text{weight flow rate} \\
\dot{W}_r &= \text{reference flow rate} \\
P_o &= \text{fore end pressure.}
\end{aligned}
$$

Figure 8.5 shows the peaking and regression of a star configuration subject to classical erosive burning. Values of K_e (erosive constant) vary from 0.3 to 1.6. Prediction of the erosive burning condition depends upon selection of a correct value for the erosive constant. Extensive tests have shown that with a correct value of K_e the above formulas describe erosive burning with a reasonable degree of accuracy. There seems to be a correlation between molecular weight, temperature, and erosive constant.

If a single motor is considered, the total effect of erosive burning will be constant. Hence K_e can be expressed in terms of this constant. Extensive tests have shown empirically that K_e can be estimated in terms of a linear equation expressed in terms of flow areas and surfaces.

Equation 8-8, when integrated in terms of rt (distance burned), with mass flow expressed in terms of burning surface by way of rt and flow area also expressed in terms of rt, yields an erosive function constant, K_3, as follows:

$$K_3 = \frac{S_o R_b \tan^{-1}[(R^2/A_f) - 1]^{1/2}}{A_f(\pi R^2 - A_f)^{1/2}}$$
$$+ \frac{(\pi R^2 - S_o R_b)\log_e(\pi R^2)}{\pi R^2 - A_f} \qquad (8\text{-}9)$$

where

R_b = burning radius
R = case radius
A_f = effective flow area.

Empirically equating statistically determined erosive burning constants for a large number of tests with varied parameters by means of the following formulation,

$$K_e = Pr^*K^*(M_o L^* T^*)^{1/4}/P^* r K_3 (T_c LM^*)^{1/4}$$
$$(8\text{-}10)$$

where

* refers to reference value
Pr = Prandtl number
P = pressure
r = burning rate
K = constant
M_o = molecular weight
L = duct length
T_c = flame temperature,

the following approximation formula is derived:

$$K_e = 0.0113 P_o(M_o)^{1/4}/K_3 r(T_c L)^{1/4} \quad (8\text{-}11)$$

where P_o = fore end pressure.

The approximation formula is useful only as an initial design formula. For de-velopment, more exact methods may be found in test and statistical studies of the particular rocket under consideration.

The erosive burning rate, r_e, equals the basic burning rate, r_o (see Fig. 8.6), plus an erosive effect, Δr (see Fig. 8.7), due to the action of the combustion gases:

$$r_e = r_o + \Delta r \qquad (8\text{-}12)$$

To determine Δr, eight variables are necessary: perimeter of core perforation (S), distance from front end of thrust chamber (Z), basic burning rate (r_o), pressure at front end of thrust chamber (P_o), erosion coefficient (K_e), flow coefficient (C_w), ratio of specific heats (γ), propellant density (d_p), and port area of section under consideration (A_p).

If S = 80 in., Z = 10 in., r_o = 0.3 ips, P_o = 1,200 psi, A_p = 90 sq in., K_e = 0.25, C_w = 0.008, γ = 1.2, and d_p = 0.05, the procedure for finding Δr is:

(1) Connect S and Z to intersect index line I; (2) connect γ and K_e to intersect index line II; (3) connect C_w and d_p to intersect index line III; (4) connect intersections on index lines II and III to intersect index line IV; (5) connect intersections on index lines I and IV to intersect index line V; (6) connect P_o and A_p to intersect index line VI; (7) connect intersections on index lines V and VI to intersect index line VII; (8) connect r_o and intersection on index line VII to find Δr, which turns out to be 6 per cent. Total burning rate, therefore, is 0.3 ips plus 6 per cent, or 0.318 ips.

Pressure variations due to burning rate changes

The relationship, $\Delta r = r_o - r_x$, relates changes of burning rate and can be expressed by the corresponding pressure ratio change. If P_o is predictable with the corresponding r_o, P_x changes as follows:

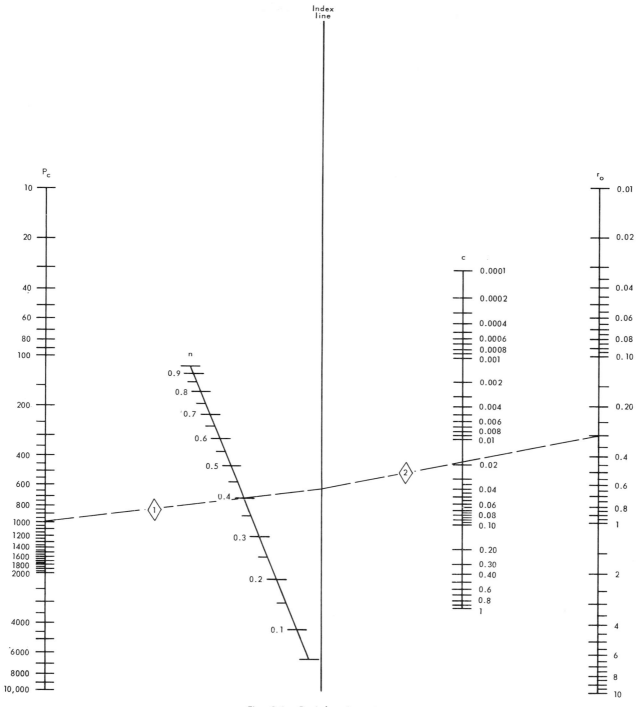

Fig. 8.6. Basic burning rate

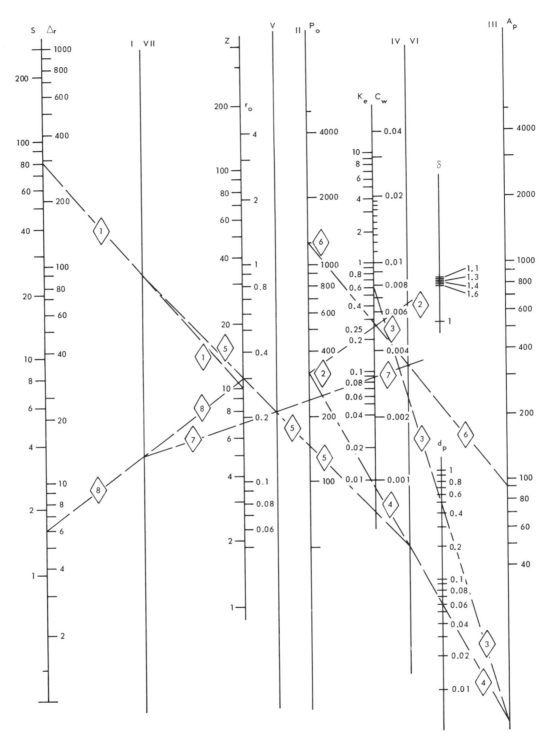

Fig. 8.7. Erosive burning rate ($r_e = r_o + \Delta r$)

TO USE: See text.

$$P_x = P_o(r_x/r_o)^{1/n} \qquad (8\text{-}13)$$

where

P_o = fore end pressure
r_o = fore end burning rate
x refers to station under study.

Application of this to temperature sensitivity gives

$$P_x = P_o(T_r - T_{px})^{1/n}/(T_r - T_{po})^{1/n} \qquad (8\text{-}14)$$

where

T_{px} = propellant temperature at station
T_{po} = propellant temperature at fore end.

This equation relates temperature sensitivity to pressure sensitivity.

Propellants with lower n values are not as sensitive to pressure changes and are therefore more desirable. Trends toward development of solid propellants with lower exponential constants aim to increase reliability (via pressure control) and to expedite design. Metal in additives are utilized to vary burning rates. The size of the metal particles determine the burning rate, whereas the additive serves other functions.

Resonant burning

Internal burning grains are subject to a critical phenomenon, apparently a function of resonance, whereby the burning rate is subject to sudden increases. Figure 8-4 illustrates resonance peaks. This unstable combustion reveals a wavy surface on the interior of cylinder grains which have been extinguished during the burn. (See Fig. 8.8, Diagram A). The waviness follows the general pattern of a wavelength and amplitude of a resonance process. The result of such resonance is unpredictable peaks of pressure which can burst the case or otherwise cause malfunction of the motor.

Correction of this condition consists of varying the over-all length of the grain, changing the perforation design, or placing a steel rod—a resonance rod—within the perforation to alter the resonance characteristics. Another method of changing the conditions of resonance is to design radial holes in the grain. Both radial holes and resonance rod are shown in Fig. 8.8, Diagram B.

Some propellants will crack as a result

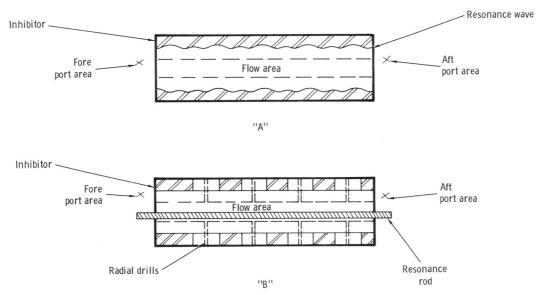

Fig. 8.8. Resonance subject grain

of resonance, and this condition in turn, by rapidly increasing the propellant burning surface, will cause extreme pressure peaks that are greater than those expected by the resonance phenomenon alone. The wavelength of resonance may be approximated by the equation

$$\lambda = 2L_g/m_o \qquad (8\text{-}15)$$

Hence the frequency becomes

$$f = \mu/\lambda = \mu m_o/2L_g \qquad (8\text{-}16)$$

where

u = velocity of wave propagation
L_g = grain length
m_o = the harmonic.

Propellants with lower specific impulse exhibit less resonance. Additives such as aluminum lower resonance. Solids of any type in the gases tend to reduce the phenomenon. In general, hotter and faster burning propellants tend to have greater resonant burning.

Ignition

The surface of the grain must be raised to the combustion temperature and a suitable chamber pressure must be by the ignitor. This device must provide this pressure and temperature over the propellant surface without undesired pressure peaks. The ignition delay should be minimized.

Ignition delay is illustrated in Figs. 8.3,

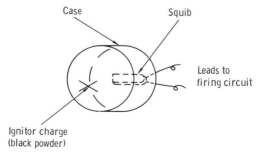

Case   Squib

Leads to
firing circuit

Ignitor charge
(black powder)

Fig. 8.9. Ignitor

8.4 and 8.5. The delay is the time to first peak.

Ignition pressure

The nozzle can be sealed during ignition to allow rapid pressurization until blow-off of the closure at 90 to 95 per cent of desired chamber pressure. The ignitor pressure from black powder can be computed as follows:

Pressure = 2,000 (powder weight in

grams/chamber volume)$^{0.86}$ (8-17)

where the volume equals the available volume, that is, the total volume minus the propellant volume. This ignitor pressure should be about one-third of the desired chamber pressure. Experiments can be made to determine quickly the pressure characteristics of other ignitor materials, such as metal powder-oxidizer charges. Black powder is commonly used as an ignitor material, but metal powders with oxidizers have smaller ignition delays (though they are somewhat more hazardous).

The general equation

$$P = k_1(W/V)^m \qquad (8\text{-}18)$$

may be used to evaluate other ignitor materials.

Ignitor components

The ignitor consists of case, ignitor material (powder, granules, or combination), and squib. Each must be designed with regard to specific requirements of the individual rocket.

Case

Plastic water-tight cases for black powder ignitors are often suitable for smaller motors. A disc shape provides simplicity of construction (see Fig. 8.9). However, as the charge size increases, the material of the case becomes an ignition hazard. (For example,

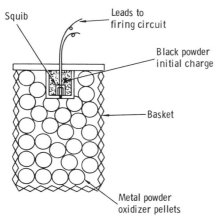

Fig. 8.10. Shotgun ignitor

if cellulose acetate is used in motors in excess of 3.5-in. diameters, plastic wall thickness becomes greater than 0.1 in., with resultant potential lodging of particles in the throat, causing rocket malfunction.) When cases constructed of tin-can material (0.01 tin-plated steel) are fired, they fragment suitably so that no large pieces are present. Standard "tin cans" used in the canning industry are sometimes ideal for certain applications utilizing black powder.

For very large rocket motors, "baskets" are utilized. The smaller black powder ignitor described above is suspended in an open mesh (metal or plastic) containing shot-gun effect pellets. This open mesh design prevents fragment hazard but requires environment control (See Figs. 8.10 and 8.11).

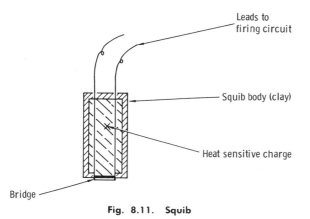

Fig. 8.11. Squib

Ignitor material

The ignitor material or charge must be suitable to the specific grain design and selection of propellant. Grains with a smaller initial burning surface do not require as great an ignitor flame distribution. Ignition temperature requirements of the propellant must also be considered. Free volume in the chamber at ignition is a factor in determining selection of ignitor material and weight of material needed to provide ignition pressure requirements.

Black powder is the most commonly used ignitor material. FFFG granulation provides suitable ignition times with minimum handling hazards. Black powder provides a high radiant transfer of energy to raise the grain surface to ignition temperature rapidly. The gaseous products of the ignitor combustion provide suitable initiation chamber pressure. This is a common material available from standard sources.

Aluminum or magnesium powder with either potassium perchlorate, ammonium perchlorate, or ammonium nitrate as oxidizer provides a higher temperature and higher energy transfer, but lower pressure, than black powder. These materials provide much shorter ignition delays. The metal-oxidizer ignitor charges, however, are more hazardous.

Compactness of any ignitor charge in terms of the firmness of contact between powder grains is directly related to time delay, and firm packing of powder to avoid voids decreases ignition delay.

Position of ignitor

The ignitor should be placed at the forward end of the motor so that the ignitor gases will flow the full length of the grain before exhausting. The ignitor reaction products must circulate over the grain surface until it is raised to ignition tempera-

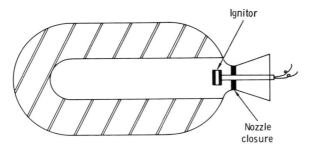

Fig. 8.12.   Aft end ignitor

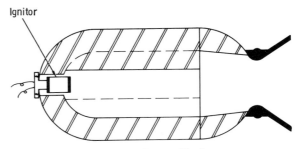

Fig. 8.13.   Fore end ignitor

Ignitor gases wash entire duct area prior to exiting through nozzle.

ture. The time required is about 5 to 15 milliseconds.

A typical ignitor is shown in Fig. 8.9. Activation of the squib (Fig. 8.11) ignites the charge, which in turn builds pressure and raises temperature of the propellant to ignition. This type of ignitor is shown in Fig. 8.12 in an aft end installation. The nozzle closure blows out at a predetermined fraction of operating pressure.

A shot gun ignitor is illustrated in Fig. 8.10. When installed as shown in Fig. 8.9, the pellets, while undergoing combustion, spread to all burning surfaces in the manner of a shot gun blast.

Sometimes, a special ignitor shape may be more suitable for a specific application. Spherical, torus, and irregular shells, cases, or baskets may be applicable. Figure 7.1 illustrates a torus ignitor that tends to spread its charge products smoothly over the exterior as well as the interior of the grain.

Fore end installation requires grain modifications to accommodate the ignitor. The star configuration with a fore end ignitor shown in Fig. 8.13 experienced a different burning curve as the result of the cylinder cut in the fore end web to allow correct placement and support for the basket ignitor.

Section III

LIQUID DESIGN

9

Systems

The components that store, feed, and burn the propellant make up the liquid engine system. Valves, tubing, tanks, and combustion devices are all considered parts of this total complex. In design, the system is usually studied in terms of

1. The tanks and/or other storage system
2. The turbopump and/or other supply system
3. The tubing and/or other feed system
4. The engine assembly, consisting of combustion chamber, injector, and nozzle
5. The valving and/or control system.

A typical large scale engine is illustrated by the model in Fig. 9.1.

In general, systems can be classified by the supply components as either a pressurized or turbopump type. Many exotic systems for both types have been proposed. Methods of canting the nozzles to provide rotary motion, or use of auxiliary rockets to provide the same motion, have been devised to drive pumps. Turbovanes have been placed in the exhaust jet. But such systems are less dependable and often more complex than turbopump systems. Turbovanes placed directly in the jet stream cause vector deflections in addition to exposing the vanes to extremely hot gases.

The degree of simplicity, reliability, and weight are the major design considerations. For low-thrust, short-duration engines, the pressurized system is preferred. For high-thrust, long-duration engines, the turbopump system is best.

The range of weight may be determined for preliminary studies from Fig. 9.2.

The gas-pressure system

The gas-pressure system is diagrammed in Fig. 9.3. A pressure generator supplies gas under pressure to the oxidizer and fuel tanks. This in turn drives the fluid through lines and valves to the injector. The pressurized propellant is injected into the combustion chamber through the injector.

Fig. 9.1. Model of J-2 200,000-lb thrust, hydrogen-fueled space engine (Courtesy, Rocketdyne)

The pressure generator, or gas-pressure supply tank, may be of various types. Helium, nitrogen, or air may be pressurized; their negligible dissolving and reacting characteristics make them suitable for such a system. Fuel and oxidizer may be burned in the generator to provide a supply of such gases; or a solid propellant charge may be utilized.

The helium, nitrogen, or air may be pressurized from 2,000 psi to above 5,000 psi as design demands. The weight of such a system becomes prohibitive as durations are extended beyond approximately one minute. A compressed gas system is best for small rockets because this arrangement lends itself well to simplified design, hence good reliability and comparatively light weight.

When the compressed gas supply metering valve is of a servo type, as needed in most compressed gas designs, searching and vibration troubles are inherent in the system. In a complex or large scale design, such a valve could be the source of, and at the same time be severely affected by, the adverse vibration complex. Resonance, resulting from utilizing such a valve, could cause combustion malfunction and/or mechanical failure.

The required gas supply can be determined from the formulas:

$$m_g = P_g V_g M_{og} / R T_g \qquad (9\text{-}1)$$

and

$$P_g V_g M_{og} / R T_g = (P_t V_t M_{ot} / R T_t) \\ \times [\gamma P_g / (P_g - P_t)] \qquad (9\text{-}2)$$

where

m_g = mass of gas supply
P_g = pressure of gas supply
P_t = pressure in propellant tank
V_g = volume of supply tank
V_t = volume of propellant tank
T_g = temperature of supply
T_t = temperature in propellant tank
γ = ratio of specific tests.

The combustion pressurized system

The combustion pressurized system needs a starter as shown in Fig. 9.4. The starter can be any of the general types of pressure generators described above or a starter valve such as a rupture diaphragm. Once the initiation pressure reaches the propellant tanks, the propellant passes through the valves to the injector and the combustion chamber. The metering valve bypasses a certain amount of fuel to the oxidizer tank and a required amount of oxidizer to the fuel tank. The controlled reactions in the storage tanks provide the continued pressure to pressurize the system after the starter has completed its function.

This type of system is subject to detonation under adverse conditions and reduction of the potency of the propellant in normal operation. Failure of a metering valve, even to a minor degree, can result in total mal-

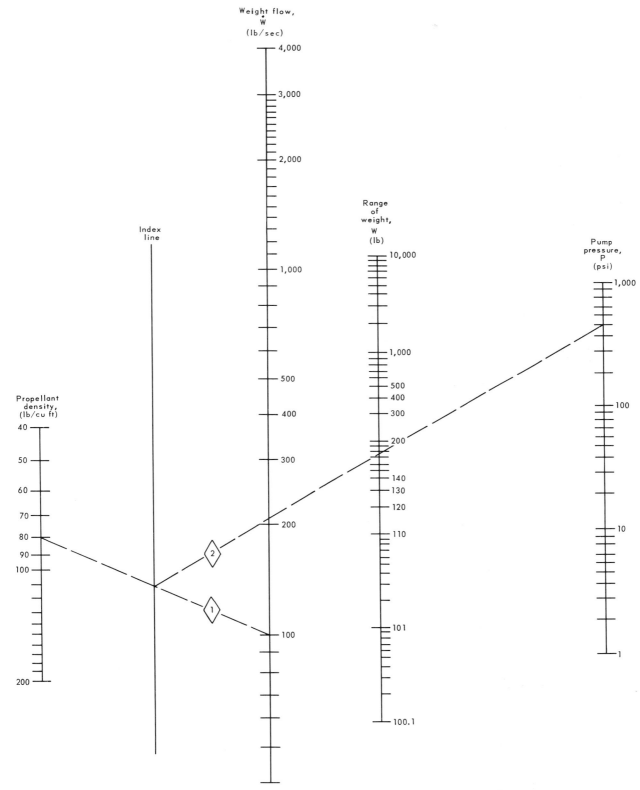

Fig. 9.2. Determining range-of-weight of turbopump system (for preliminary design)

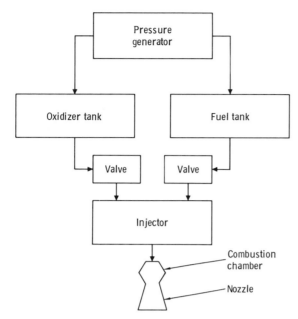

Fig. 9.3. Pressurized propellant system

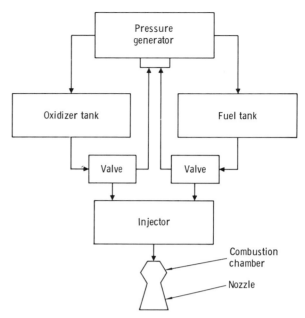

Fig. 9.5. Feedback pressure generator

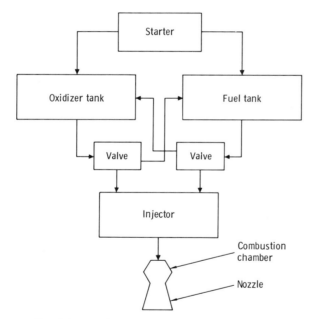

Fig. 9.4. Combustion pressurized propellant system

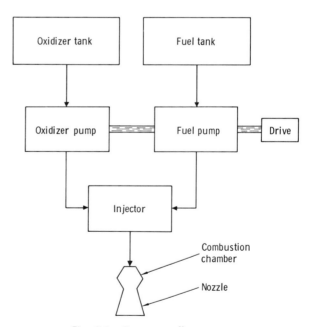

Fig. 9.6. Pump propellant system

function. Feedback and vibration parameters are critical.

Feedback pressure generator

The feedback pressure system, a bootstrap operation, is illustrated in Fig. 9.5.

Initiation pressure drives the propellant through the valves. A metered amount is directed to the pressure generator, where reaction occurs, providing greater pressure, which in turn provides greater flow. This cycle continues until the rated system flow is reached.

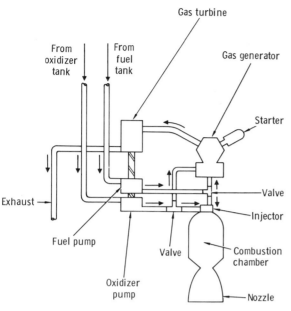

Fig. 9.7. Gas turbopump engine

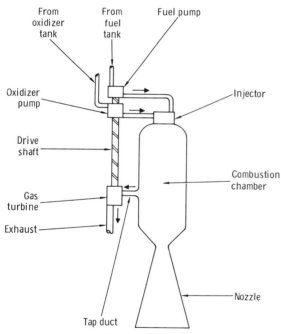

Fig. 9.8. Gas tap turbopump engine

Turbopump system

The essentials of the pump system are shown in Fig. 9.6. The propellants are stored in their respective tanks. Feed lines direct the fluids to the pumps, which in turn drive the propellants to the injector and the combustion chamber. The drive can be provided by a number of methods. However, the most practical is the gas turbine.

Gas generators may be utilized to drive the turbine wheels. Figure 9.7 illustrates the standard arrangement. A starter is used to begin the cycle, and propellant is tapped from the valves to continue the operation. The gas generator provides gases to the gas turbine, which in turn drives the pumps.

Solid propellant gas generators may be used instead of the starter and generator shown in Fig. 9.7. When a solid propellant is utilized, the starter and generator are essentially identical. The solid charge builds up to operating pressure and continues to supply gas to the turbine throughout operation of the liquid engine.

Gas may also be tapped directly from the combustion chamber to drive the turbine. This provides a certain simplicity of design. Figure 9.8 illustrates a gas tap turbopump engine. The hot gases are taken directly from the combustion chamber, cooled, then fed into the gas turbine.

The turbine exhaust is usually directed through a nozzle to provide a slight thrust augmentation and to stabilize the exit pressure of the turbine.

Heat exchange "pumps"

Figure 9.9 illustrates a heat exchange pump. This type includes pressurization systems that provide gases to the propellant tanks by heating the propellants with the heat exchangers. This "boiler" principle is commonly used to inject water into steam boilers. The pump in Fig. 9.9 shows a different arrangement, however, in which the heat transferred to the propellants is converted to velocity and pressure. The heated fluids are fed directly into the injector and then to the combustion chamber.

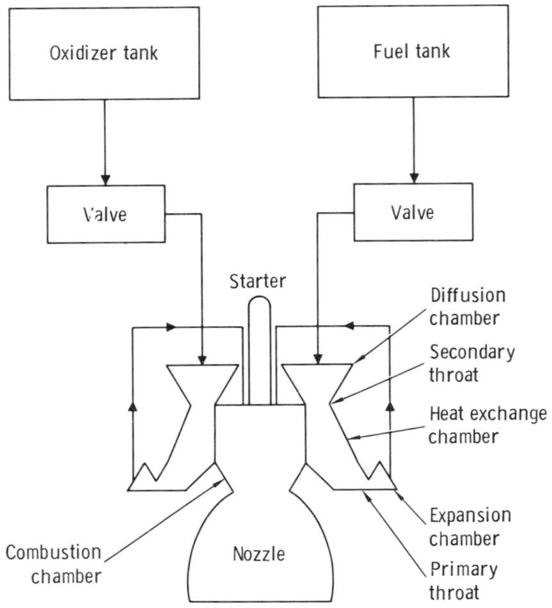

Fig. 9.9   Heat exchanger pump propellant system

These "pumps" have limited application. Pressure conditions are not always suitable. A comparatively large starter must also be used. Weight parameters are apt to be critical.

Variable thrust systems

Variable thrust and on-off capability are requirements in the design of many engines. Some propellants can be fully controlled by valves of the type used to control jet engine fuels. However, many rocket oxidizers and fuels cannot be easily metered. Positive valves must be used with such propellants.

In some instances, a degree of variability can be obtained (10 to 99 per cent) by valve controls, whereas the flow cannot be completely stopped without positive on-off valves. Figure 9.10 illustrates a variable thrust system with positive on-off capabilities. With reference to the fuel line, it is seen that when the on-valve opens first in the line (for example, when a rupture disc bursts), the flow passes through the off-valve

to the variable valve and then to the injector. The variable flow valve provides limited control.

When the off-valve is activated, the flow stops completely. The restart may be accomplished by activating the second on-valve on the bypass line.

Weight of systems

In order to evaluate any of these systems in terms of efficiency, missions, or other parameters, reasonable estimation of weight must be made. Figure 9.2 allows preliminary design weight determination of turbo-pump systems. For scaling up established designs or prototypes, Figs. 9.11 and 9.12 provide a simplified method. To estimate the throat area of such scaled-up designs, Fig. 9.11 may be used. The throat areas and the thrust of the *model* are entered on the left side, and by entering the required thrust of the *scaled-up* prototype on the right side, the scaled-up size of the throat may be determined. To estimate the inert weight of such scaled-up designs, Fig. 9.12 may be used. These two graphs allow estimation from different parameters. For more detailed estimation, the tubing weight may be estimated from Fig. 9.13, and the storage tank weight and

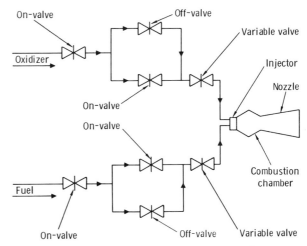

Fig. 9.10.   Variable thrust system with on-off capability

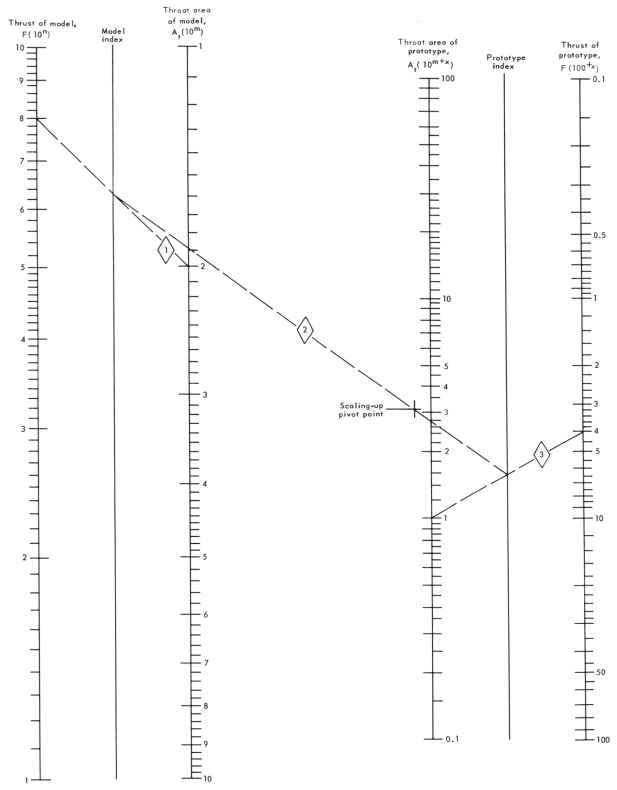

Fig. 9.11. Scaling-up nomograph

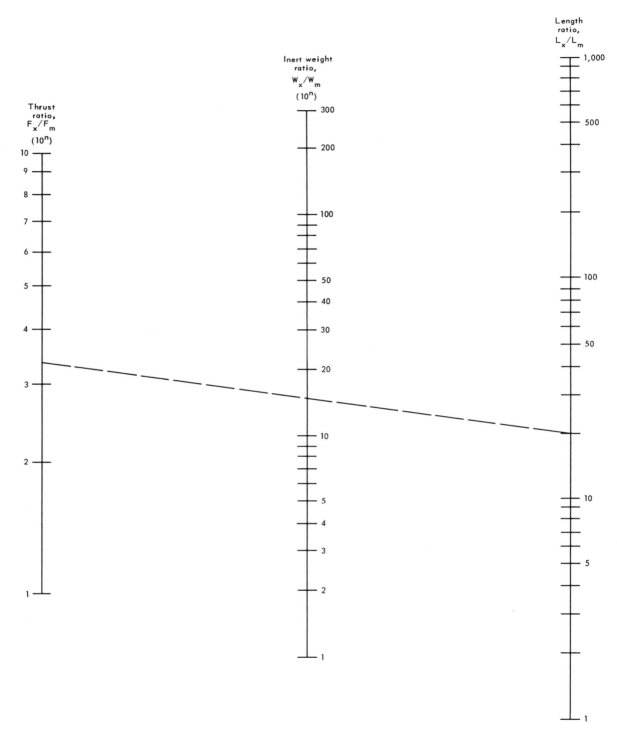

Fig. 9.12. Approximation of inert weight ratio of scaled-up design

Graph allows only a rough approximation. (Exact values must be determined by studies of the system in "scaled-up" detail analysis.) Example: What is inert weight ratio of million-pound thrust design scaled up from 33,000-lb thrust design if length is to be 20 times as great? Answer from centerline: 150.

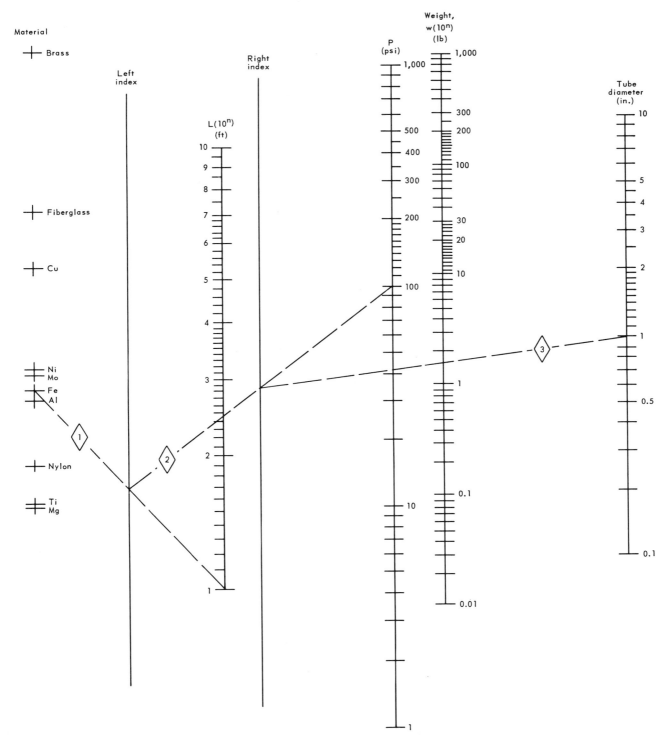

Fig. 9.13. Tubing weight

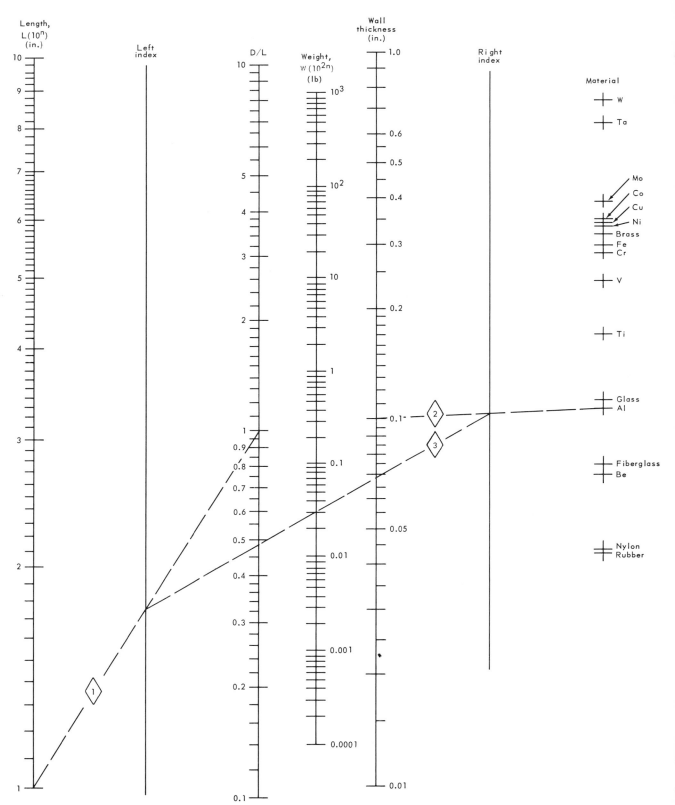

Fig. 9.14. Estimated weight of combustion chamber or storage tank

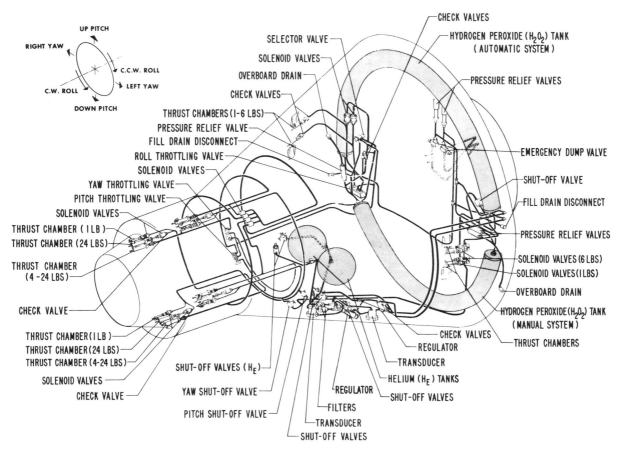

Fig. 9.15. Reaction control system for Mercury project liquid rockets, showing pitch, roll, and yaw correction

Control rockets consist of small reaction jets with thrusts ranging from 1 to 24 lb. Some are throttleable as indicated.

the combustion chamber weight may be estimated from Fig. 9.14.

Figure 9.15 illustrates a small-scale system for reaction control. Comparison of this system with Fig. 9.1 shows the extremes of application. This system is a very small-thrust pressurized system, whereas Fig. 9.1 is a high-thrust turbo-pump system.

10

Liquid Propellant Properties

The major properties of fifteen oxidizers and forty-four fuels most commonly considered as propellants (in various combinations) are presented in this chapter in condensed chart form (Tables 10.1—10.6). Thus, approximate design parameters may be considered prior to more extensive study of the specified selected propellant combination.

High-energy oxidizers must be studied to determine the structural material for the system. Passivation may be used for highly reactive oxidizers. Pure aluminum and selected stainless steel are best for containers and as construction materials for hydrogen peroxide, oxygen, and ozone.

Fluorine, a high-performance oxidizer, is by far the most reactive. It reacts with water, nitric acid, wood, hydrogen, concrete, and even asbestos. Exposure to this yellow liquid or green yellow gas will cause aluminum and steel to burn vigorously. It is an extreme fire hazard in both the liquid and gaseous states. However, although fluorine will react with copper, monel, stainless steel, nickel, carbon steel, and aluminum, all these materials may still be utilized for fluorine systems if they are first passivated by allowing an inert metal fluoride film to be developed on all exposed surfaces, including lines, valves, and pumps. Contaminants and other potential causes of local temperature increases must be completely avoided. The system temperature must be maintained below the reaction temperature. In general, fluorine is a hypergolic oxidizer. Similar care should be exercised in the use of other high energy oxidizers such as oxygen.

Propellant toxicity must always be considered in propellant selection. For example, eye contact with fluorine gas can lead to blindness; inhalation can be fatal within 30 minutes if concentrations exceed 50 ppm; skin contact can result in severe burns.

Temperature ranges of specific propellants must be thoroughly considered for storage. Where indicated, cyrogenic temperature ranges must be sustained and the effects throughout the system incorporated in the design. Hydrogen peroxide, for example, will decompose to oxygen and superheated steam at temperatures above 350°F. Once this occurs, spontaneous explosions are possible. Propellant temperature ranges are indicated on the propellant liquid state charts in Figs. 10.6 and 10.7. Other properties may be determined by selection of coding from the listing in Table 10.1 and by using the selected codes in Tables 10.2—10.6.

With a knowledge of the chart values, the following figures may be used:

Figure 10.1 may be used to determine the specific impulse with the design chamber pressure and fuel ratio. Tables 10.1 and 10.5 give values for $f(I_{sp})$ and $\dot{r}_{opt}$, respectively.

Figure 10.2 allows determination of fuel and oxidizer density at design temperature.

Figure 10.3 allows estimation of the bulk specific gravity based on the density values from Fig. 10.2.

Figure 10.4 provides viscosity values for use in hydraulic computations.

Figure 10.5 provides a range of typical specific impulse values that may be used for preliminary design calculations.

Figure 10.6 presents the range of liquid-to-gas states of oxidizers.

Figure 10.7 presents the range of liquid-to-gas states of fuels.

Figure 10.8 presents vapor pressures at different temperatures for oxidizers.

Figure 10.9 presents vapor pressures at different temperatures for fuels.

Figure 10.10 provides density values and range of operating temperature for the liquids.

Table 10.1.   Propellant properties coding for Tables 10.2—10.6

OXIDIZERS

Code A—Bromine pentafluoride
Code B—Chlorine trifluoride
Code C—Hydrogen peroxide
Code D—Nitrogen tetroxide
Code E—Nitrogen trifluoride
Code F—Fluorine
Code G—ON 7030
Code H—Ozone

Code J—Oxygen difluoride
Code K—Perchloryl fluoride
Code L—RFNA (6.5%)
Code M—RFNA (16%)
Code N—WFNA
Code O—Oxygen
Code P—Tetranitromethane

FUELS

Code 1—Acetylene
Code 2—Aluminum borohydride
Code 3—Ammonia
Code 4—Aniline
Code 5—Benzene
Code 6—Butyl Mercaptan
Code 7—Diborane
Code 8—Diethylenetriamine (DELTA)
Code 9—Ethane
Code 10—Ethyl alcohol
Code 11—Ethylamine
Code 12—Ethylene
Code 13—Ethylene diamine
Code 14—Ethylene oxide
Code 15—Ethyl nitrate

Code 16—Furfuryl alcohol
Code 17—Gasoline
Code 18—Heptane
Code 19—Hydrazine
Code 20—Hydrogen
Code 21—Isopropyl alcohol
Code 22—JP-3
Code 23—JP-4
Code 24—Kerosene
Code 25—Lithium
Code 26—Lithium hydride
Code 27—Methane
Code 28—Methylal
Code 29—Methyl alcohol
Code 30—Methylamine

Code 31—Nitromethane
Code 32—Nitropropane
Code 33—n-octane
Code 34—Propane
Code 35—n-propyl nitrate
Code 36—o-toluidine
Code 37—Triethylamine
Code 38—Trimethyl trithiophosphite
Code 39—Turpentine
Code 40—Unsymmetrical dimethyl hydrazine (UDMH)
Code 41—2, 3-xylidene
Code 42—Lithium borohydride
Code 43—Monomethylhydrazine (MMH)
Code 44—Pentaborane

Liquid Propellant Properties

Table 10.2. $f(I_{sp})_1$ values for Figure 10.1															
Oxidizers															
Fuels	A	B	C	D	E	F	G	H	J	K	L	M	N	O	P
1				1.34										1.18	
2			1.87											1.06	
3	1.65	1.6		1.48		.85	1.5	1.74	1.08					1.34	
4				1.66								1.65	1.64		
5				1.82											
6													1.52		
7						.92									
8	1.95	1.52		1.42										1.6	
9														1.4	
10												1.77		1.53	
11				1.68											
12														1.3	
13														1.5	
14							1.5							1.38	
15															
16													1.86		
17													1.73	1.43	
18															
19	1.8	1.6	1.55	1.48	1.3	.94		1.16	.9	1.31	1.54	1.52	1.5	1.3	1.4
20				1.15		.3	.2						.94	.5	
21			1.63	1.71		1.2	1.2				1.78			1.54	
22			1.63	1.65		1.2	1.2					1.76	1.65	1.44	
23			1.63	1.65		1.2						1.76	1.65	1.44	
24														1.45	
25						.57								.75	
26														1.26	
27														1.32	
28														1.58	
29		1.79				.96							1.78	1.5	
30														1.58	
31														1.49	
32														1.94	
33			1.65	1.68					1		1.74			1.46	
34				1.55											
35															
36												1.8			
37															
38							1.67					1.76			
39				1.74			1.5					1.64	1.6	1.65	
40	1.84	1.4	1.4	1.34		.82			.90	1.32	1.3	1.5	1.55	1.39	

Table 10.2. $f(I_{sp})_1$ values for Figure 10.1 (Continued)															
Oxidizers															
Fuels	A	B	C	D	E	F	G	H	J	K	L	M	N	O	P
41				1.72											
42														.82	
43	1.82	1.37		1.32											
44	1.62	1.42	1.2	1.25	1.16	.7			.6	1.15				0.95	

Table 10.3. Approximate average molecular weights of combustion gas															
Oxidizers															
Fuels	A	B	C	D	E	F	G	H	J	K	L	M	N	O	P
1															
2															
3	29	22				19	21		18		21	21	25	19	
4											25	25			
5															
6													27		
7						21									
8														21	
9															
10			23								25	25		23	
11															
12															
13														19	
14							24							22	
15															
16															
17														23	
18															
19		23	19	19		19			18		20	20	25	17	20
20						9								9	
21														22	
22			22			24		21				25		22	
23			22			24		21				25		22	
24			22											22	
25															
26															
27															
28															
29														22	

Liquid Propellant Properties

Table 10.3. Approximate average molecular weights of combustion gas (Continued)

Fuels	\<Oxidizers\> A	B	C	D	E	F	G	H	J	K	L	M	N	O	P
30														20	
31															
32														23	
33							20				24			22	
34															
35															
36															
37						25									
38						30					30				
39						24					26	26	25	22	
40											22	22	22	20	
41															
42															

Table 10.4. Approximate ratios of specific heats

Fuels	\<Oxidizers\> A	B	C	D	E	F	G	H	J	K	L	M	N	O	P
1														1.27	
2															
3	1.34	1.32				1.33	1.23	1.23	1.29		1.24	1.24	1.24	1.23	
4											1.23	1.23	1.23		
5															
6											1.22	1.22	1.22		
7						1.31									
8														1.24	
9															
10			1.2											1.2	
11															
12															
13														1.23	
14							1.24							1.24	
15															
16														1.22	
17														1.2	
18															
19		1.33	1.25	1.26		1.33			1.28		1.25	1.25	1.25	1.25	1.27
20						1.33								1.26	

Table 10.4. Approximate ratios of specific heats (Continued)															
	Oxidizers														
Fuels	A	B	C	D	E	F	G	H	J	K	L	M	N	O	P
21														1.22	
22			1.2			1.22		1.25			1.23	1.23	1.23	1.24	
23			1.2			1.22		1.25			1.23	1.23	1.23	1.24	
24			1.2											1.24	
25															
26															
27															
28															
29							1.23							1.21	
30														1.22	
31														1.23	
32														1.23	
33									1.3		1.24	1.24	1.24	1.23	
34															
35															
36															
37															
38							1.23				1.21	1.21	1.21		
39							1.25				1.22	1.22	1.22	1.23	
40											1.23	1.23	1.23	1.24	
41															
42															

Table 10.5. Flame temperature at near optimum fuel ratios ($^0F \times 10^3$)															
	Oxidizers														
Fuels	A	B	C	D	E	F	G	H	J	K	L	M	N	O	P
1				5.87										6.0	
2			5.77											6.0	
3	6.66	5.00		4.6		7.5	4.9	5.2	6.0					4.8	
4				5.75								5.0	4.95		
5				5.6											
6													6.0		
7						7.9									
8														6.5	
9														5.3	
10												4.6		5.3	
11				5.55											

Table 10.5. Flame temperature at near optimum fuel ratios ($^\circ$F X 10^3) (Continued)															
Oxidizers															
Fuels	A	B	C	D	E	F	G	H	J	K	L	M	N	O	P
12														5.5	
13														6.0	
14						5.7								5.75	
15															
16													4.9		
17													4.9	5.7	
18															
19		6.0	4.7	4.9		7.75		5.42	6.4		4.4	4.7	4.7	5.4	5.3
20				5.6		8.5		4.3					5.4	5.9	
21				4.8							4.8			5.6	
22			4.8	5.5		7.1		6.4				5.2	5.0	5.9	
23			4.8	5.5		7.1		6.4				5.2	5.0	5.9	
24			4.3											5.2	
25						7.0		14						13.	
26														6.4	
27														4.9	
28														5.1	
29		5.1				7.5							4.5	5.1	
30														5.6	
31														4.7	
32														5.6	
33			4.1	4.9					7.4		5.0			5.5	
34				5.1											
35															
36												4.9			
37															
38							6.0					5.5			
39				5.55			5.8					5.5	5.0	5.9	
40												5.2	5.1	5.65	
41				5.5											
42														8.3	

Table 10.6. Near Optimum Fuel Ratios (r̂)

Fuels	A	B	C	D	E	F	G	H	J	K	L	M	N	O	P
1				3										1.23	
2			3											1.32	
3	6	3		2		2.9	2.1	1.1	1.9					1.25	
4				3.9								3	3		
5				4.4											
6													4.2		
7						5									
8	3.7	2.9		2.9										1.5	
9														2.3	
10												2.5		1.5	
11				4											
12														1.9	
13														1.4	
14							2							1.1	
15															
16													2.65		
17													4.6	2.3	
18															
19	2.2	68	1.7	1	2.6	2		.64	1.1	1.1	1	1.2	1.22	.83	1.4
20				11		10		2.7				12.5	12.5	3.5	
21				3		3.6		2			3.3	3.4	3.5	1.8	1.8
22			6.5	3		3		2.4			4	4.1	4.7	2.3	
23			6.5	3		3		2.4			4	4.1	4.7	2.3	
24														2.3	
25						2.2								1.2	
26														1.3	
27														2.3	
28														1	
29		2.9				2.4							2.4	1.2	
30														2	
31														.08	
32														.9	
33			5	3					3.8		4.5			2.3	
34				4.2											
35															
36												3			
37															
38							2.5					3			
39				4.7			3.5					4.2	4.4	2.4	
40	3.7	3		2.6					1.8	2.6		2.6	2.7	1.4	

Liquid Propellant Properties

Table 10.6. Near Optimum Fuel Ratios ($\dot{r}$) (Continued)															
Oxidizers															
Fuels	A	B	C	D	E	F	G	H	J	K	L	M	N	O	P
41				3											
42														1.5	
43	3.6	3		2.2											
44	11	7	2	3											

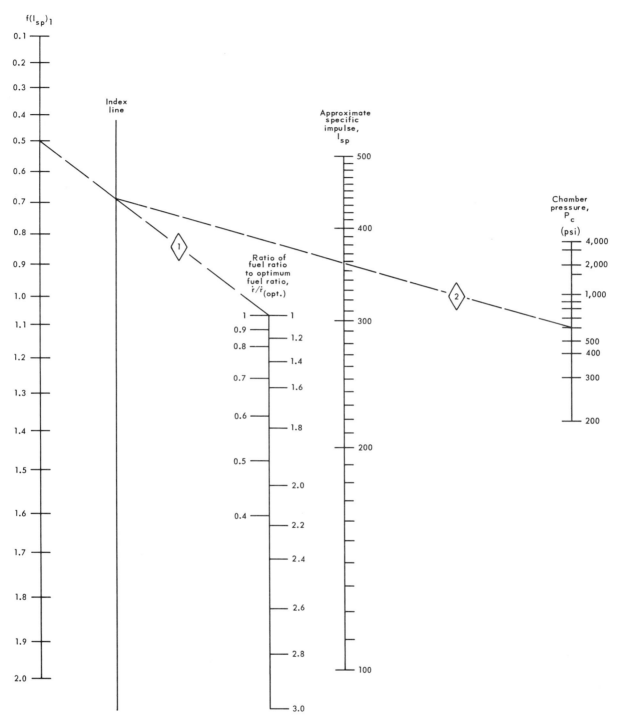

Fig. 10.1. Liquid engine specific impulse estimation

$f(I_{sp})$ *is obtained from Table 10.1 and* r_{opt} *from Table 10.5.*

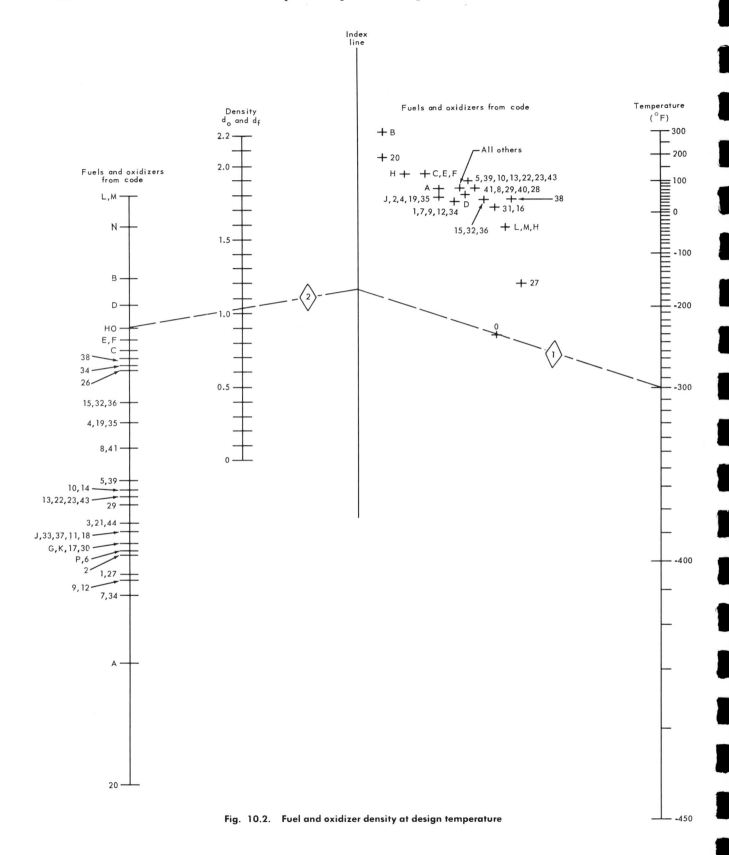

Fig. 10.2.   Fuel and oxidizer density at design temperature

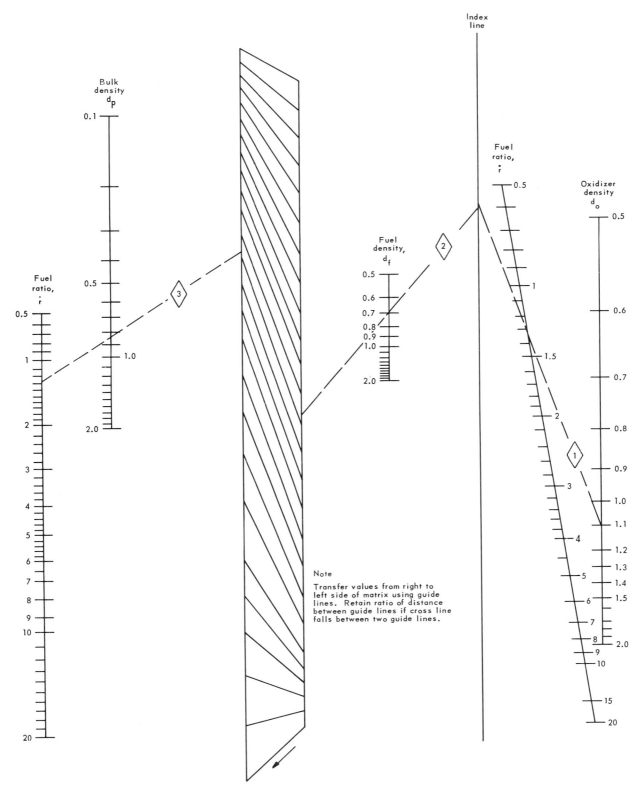

Fig. 10.3. Bulk specific gravity

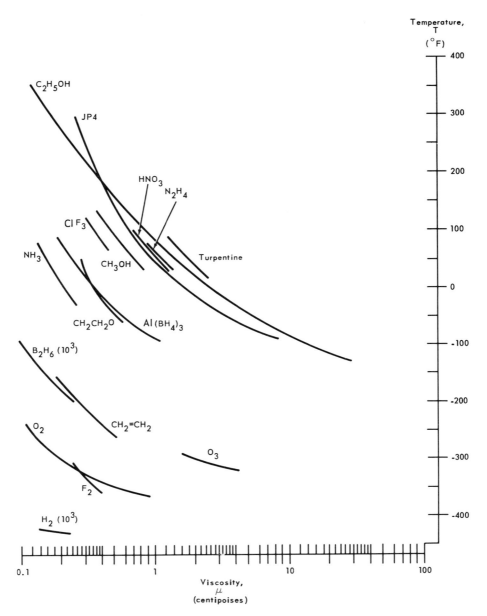

Fig. 10.4. Viscosity

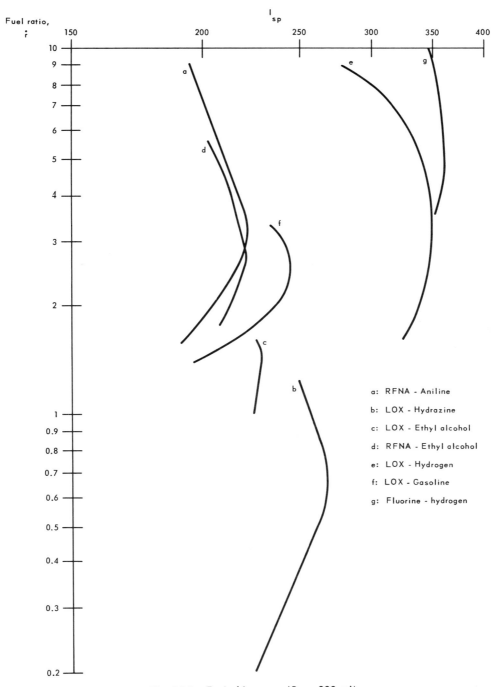

Fig. 10.5. Typical I_{sp} curves ($P_c = 300$ psi)

Liquid Propellant Properties

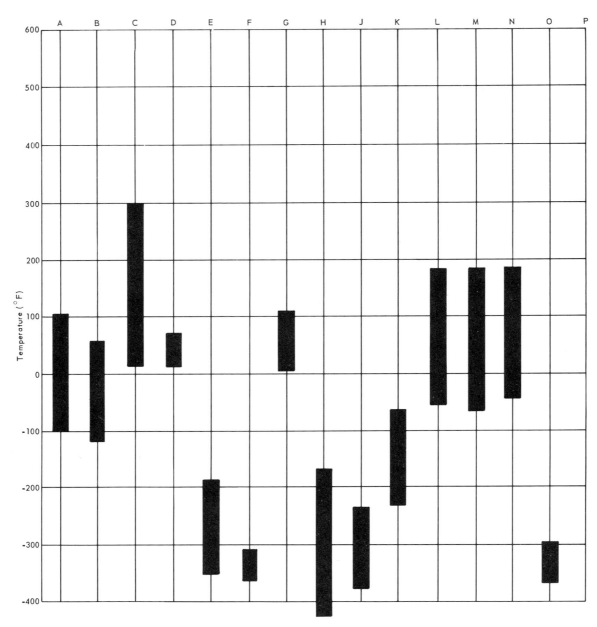

Fig. 10.6. Propellant liquid state of oxidizers from freezing to normal boiling points

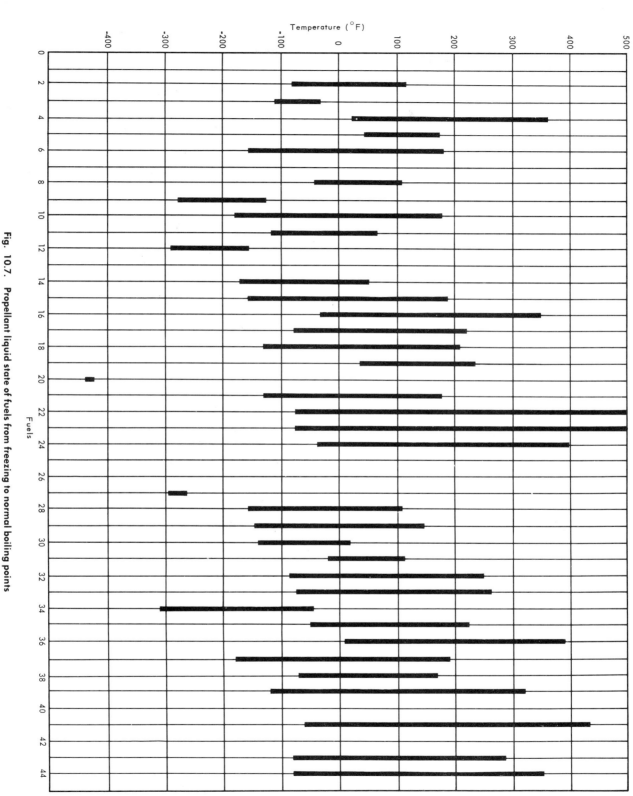

Temperature (°F)

Fig. 10.7.   Propellant liquid state of fuels from freezing to normal boiling points

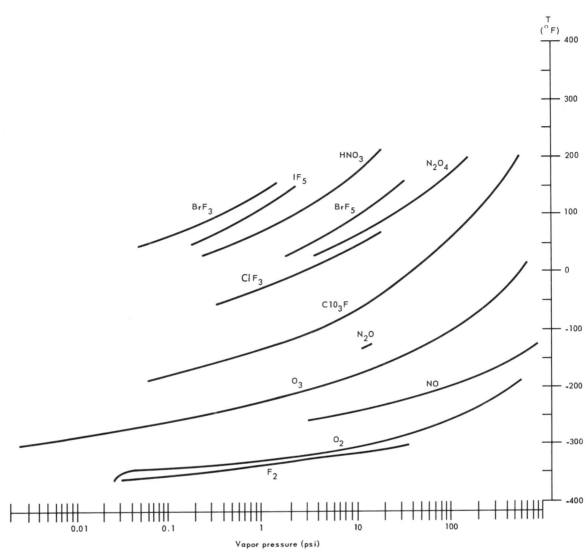

Fig. 10.8. Oxidizer vapor pressures

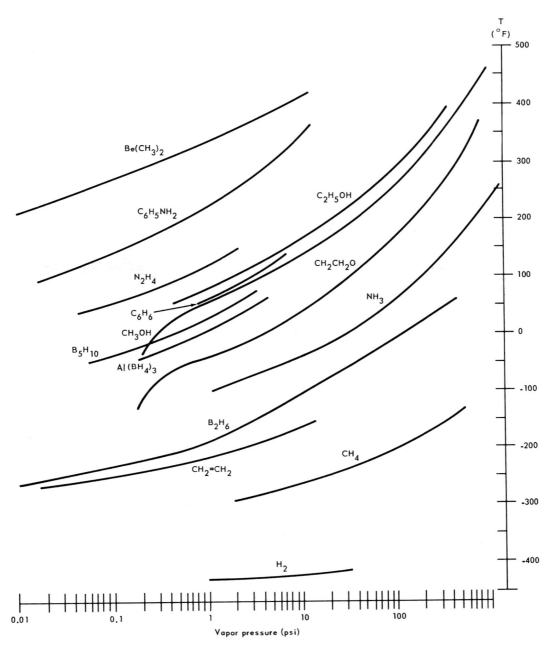

Fig. 10.9.   Fuel vapor pressures

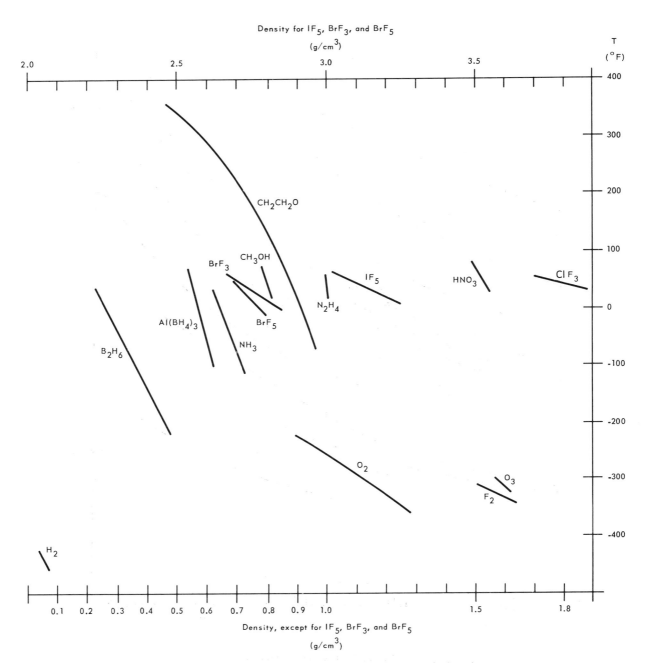

Fig. 10.10.   Density values and operating temperatures for liquids

11

Combustion Chamber and
System Pressure Losses

Configuration

The nozzle and combustion chamber are the heart of the liquid rocket engine system. Performance depends upon their design configuration. If the chamber does not provide sufficient length for complete reaction, the specific impulse will be only a fraction of the computed value. If the chamber should be too long or too large, the reaction will be complete, but the weight penalty will reduce over-all performance. Usually the chamber configuration is that of a cylinder closed at one end by the injector and fore end head and at the other by the nozzle and aft end head.

The standard De Laval nozzle and chamber are illustrated in Fig. 11.1. Plug nozzle design is illustrated in Fig. 11.2.

Pressure

The pressure of a liquid propellant engine must be sufficient to fill the nozzle and insure good burning, yet must be low enough not to require excess weight of pressurizing system or chamber wall. The aim of chamber design is to produce maximum thrust conditions while minimizing weight, without sacrificing reliability. The pressure can be determined from the following equation if desired weight flow and throat area are known:

$$P_c = (\dot{W}_o + \dot{W}_f)/C_w A_t \qquad (11\text{-}1)$$

where

$\dot{W}_o$ = oxidizer flow rate
$\dot{W}_f$ = fuel flow rate.

It may also be calculated directly from the thrust:

$$P_c = F/C_f A_t \qquad (11\text{-}2)$$

A design pressure may be selected first and the required throat area found by means of Equation 11-2. The required weight flow may be found by means of Equation 11-1. Usually, combustion pressures range from 300 to 800 psi. Selection should be based on the following:

1. The best pressure for combustion, if such exists, and the pressure limits, if they exist
2. The requirements of the turbopump or other pressurizing system
3. Chamber and nozzle stresses
4. Chemical equilibrium requirements
5. The thrust and weight flow
6. The ambient pressure at operating altitude.

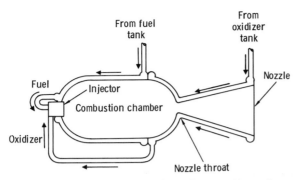

Fig. 11.1.   Regenerative cooling of De Laval nozzle and chamber

Equation 11-3 indicates the relationship of chamber pressure to other rocket parameters:

$$I_{sp} = 6.93\phi[(2T_c\gamma)/M_o(\gamma - 1)]^{1/2} \times$$
$$[1 - (P_e/P_c)^{(\gamma-1)/\gamma}]^{1/2} \qquad (11\text{-}3)$$

where

γ = ratio of specific heats
ϕ = loss factor
T_c = chamber temperature
M_o = molecular weight of the combustion gases
P_e = pressure at the nozzle exhaust
P_c = chamber pressure.

Stress in the chamber or nozzle wall may be estimated by the basic equation:

$$S = D(D - d)^{-1}(P_c - P_{cool}) \qquad (11\text{-}4)$$

where

D = outside diameter
d = inside diameter
P_c = chamber pressure
P_{cool} = coolant pressure.

This may be maximum before ignition when P_c equals zero, during steady state combustion, or at some other time. Stress must be considered under every condition.

Characteristic chamber length

The characteristic chamber length, L^*, is a hypothetical length associated with the operational characteristics of a given chamber. It provides an indication of the effective length of a chamber in terms of the requirements of the chemical reaction:

$$L^* = V_c/A_t \qquad (11\text{-}5)$$

where

V_c = volume of chamber
A_t = throat area.

Thus L^* is the length that would be exhibited by another chamber having the same volume and throat area but designed as a tube with its cross-sectional area equal to the throat area. If an engine required a 60-in. characteristic length to insure combustion, the physical length, therefore, might be only a fraction of that.

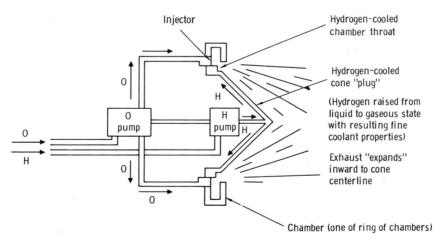

Fig. 11.2.   H-O plug nozzle

Design consists of ring of small, independent, high-pressure chambers with sonic conditions at throat.

Stay time

The stay time of a gas is the time required for total combustion to occur and can be estimated analytically or by combustion experiments with the proper combination. Estimates may also be made for propellant combinations from Fig. 11.3.

The chamber design must provide for stay time, as well as time for evaporation, mixing, and any other required phenomena other than actual reaction. The design stay time includes all such time functions.

Stay time may be estimated from a number of equations which are developed from the volume–weight flow relationship:

$$t_s = V_c / \dot{W} v \qquad (11\text{-}6)$$

where

$$t_s = \text{stay time}$$
$$V_c = \text{chamber volume}$$
$$v = \text{average specific volume of propellant gases in chamber}$$
$$\dot{W} = \text{propellant flow rate.}$$

In terms of temperature and molecular weight, this can be expressed as

$$t_s = M_o V_c P_c / 12 \, \dot{W} R T_c \qquad (11\text{-}7)$$

where

$$R = \text{universal gas constant.}$$

If the time for vaporization and mixing is neglected, the following expression in terms of propellant properties and chamber geometry may be used:

$$t_s = V_c (M_o^{1/2}) A_t^{-1} (gRT_c)^{-1/2} (\gamma)^{-1/2} \times$$
$$[(\gamma + 1)/2]^{(\gamma+1)/2(\gamma-1)} \qquad (11\text{-}8)$$

The design stay time may be easily estimated from Fig. 11.3, or the above equation. A more exact equation follows:

$$t_s = \left[\frac{(L^*)^m M_o^{1/2}}{f(T_c) f(Q)} \right] \left[1 - \frac{1.9879}{C_p} \right]^{1/2} \times$$
$$\left[\left(\frac{V_c P_c^q}{F} \right)^m \left(\frac{gR}{T_c} \right)^{1/2} \right] \left[\left(\frac{\gamma + 1}{2} \right)^{(\gamma+1)/(\gamma-1)} \right]^{1/2} (11\text{-}9)$$

where

$$f(T_c) = \text{function of chamber temperature}$$
$$f(Q) = \text{heat function}$$
$$m, g = \text{experimental constants}$$
$$q = \text{pressure exponent}$$
$$F = \text{thrust.}$$

A rapid but inaccurate approximation for initial design calculations may be made by the following:

$$t_s \cong 5 \, L^* \, C^* \qquad (11\text{-}10)$$

where C^* is the characteristic velocity.

Stay time requirements may be lessened in large-scale engines due to the reduction of chamber volume needed to insure total combustion, as indicated by experiments which give the following relationship:

$$V_c = C_q (A_t / P_c^m) \qquad (11\text{-}11)$$

where

$$C_q = \text{an experimental constant}$$
$$m = \text{an experimental exponent } (m > 1).$$

Chamber volume and area exposed to combustion gas

The chamber volume and exposed area must be determined from the exact geometry of the chamber and nozzle; however, for preliminary design, or the use of a true cylinder and standard nozzle, the following formulations may be utilized:

For the chamber areas exposed to gas:

$$A_c \cong \pi L_c D_c - A_t + (\pi D_c^2 / 2) \quad (11\text{-}12)$$

where

$$L_c = \text{chamber length}$$
$$D_c = \text{chamber diameter.}$$

For the chamber volume:

$$V_c = (\pi D_c^2 / 4)[L_c + (2D_c / 3)] \quad (11\text{-}13)$$

Stress may be studied with the cylinder stress charts in Chapter 18.

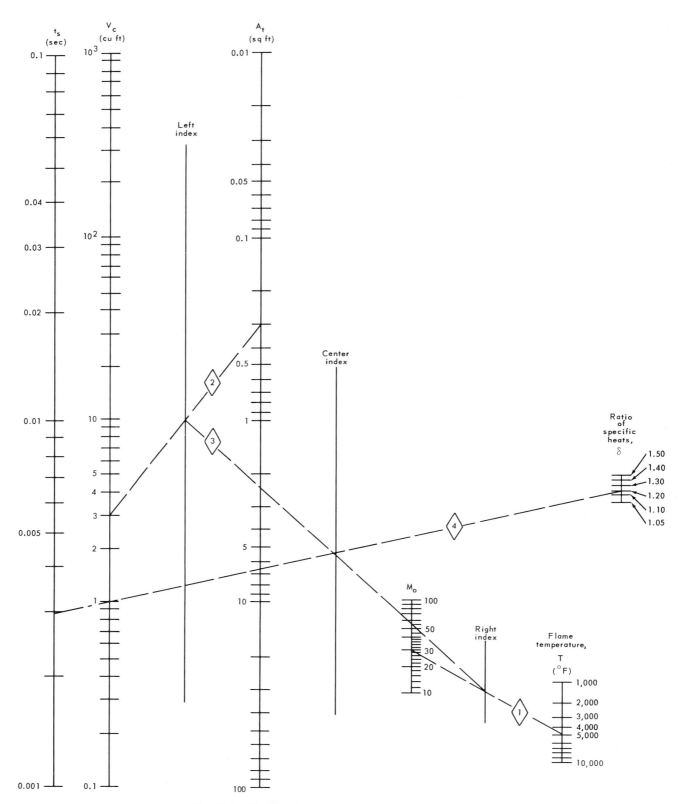

Fig. 11.3.   Liquid rocket engine combustion chamber stay time

System pressure losses

Estimation of pressure losses in regeneratively cooled rocket chambers and nozzles depends upon the values selected or computed for the friction loss coefficient, f, in the following equation:

$$\Delta P = f d L (V^2)(2gD)^{-1} \qquad (11\text{-}14)$$

where

ΔP = pressure loss
f = friction loss coefficient
d = coolant density
L = length of coolant passage
V = coolant velocity
g = acceleration of gravity
D = equivalent diameter of the flow passage.

Regenerative cooling is accomplished by utilizing the fuel, oxidizer, or both, to cool the nozzle and chamber prior to combustion. The heat removed in cooling is utilized in the combustion process—hence the term regenerative cooling. Chamber and nozzle passages are complex structures compared with simple tubing. Figure 11.1 illustrates a typical regenerative cooling arrangement. In this diagram, fuel is used to cool the chamber while oxidizer is used to cool the nozzle. The fuel is pumped from the fuel tank via the turbopump, passes over the surface of the combustion chamber (reducing the temperature to within material limits), then is injected into the combustion chamber. While the fuel is cooling the surface of the combustion chamber, the oxidizer cools the nozzle. As each fluid reduces the temperature of the respective part of the engine, it becomes heated, and this heat is returned to the reaction. The amount of fuel and oxidizer can be related to the fuel ratio by means of Fig. 11.4.

The flow passage in both chamber and nozzle is not actually as simple as illustrated. The nozzle tubes, for example, can be in the form of helical coils. Other configurations, such as rectangular ducts, can also be utilized. Each shape evidences a different friction loss coefficient; f is also affected, somewhat, by the fluid temperature. Tube curvature increases the value of f roughly as the square of the ratio of the angle of curvature to 90 degrees $(\theta/90°)^2$, thus increasing the complexities of computation. Surface texture of the flow passage must be considered also.

To determine the correct friction loss coefficient, f, the parameters of the passage must be examined in terms of Figs. 11.5–11.8.

Figure 11.5 provides for the effect of the relative smoothness of the passage surface. To use the chart: (1) Establish the value of the texture by selecting the "condition of surface" point. (2) With the correct perimeter value on the Z line, use a ruler to index the surface texture value, $\dot{\phi}_m$. In the example shown, the value of $\dot{\phi}_m$ is 8. With this value, the friction prime factor, f', can be found from Fig. 11.6.

From Fig. 11.6 the Reynolds number (Re) can be determined, as well as the f' value. If no curvature exists, $f' = f$; but if curvature is present, Fig. 11.7 can be used to estimate the curvature function, $F(k)$, which in turn can be used in Fig. 11.8 to compute graphically the increased value of the friction coefficient, f.

In these charts, use of the flow perimeter and the flow area compensates for variation of configuration. Consideration of the viscosity compensates for temperature variation effects. The $F(k)$ function allows for curvature. With proper consideration of the variation of areas, lengths, perimeters, etc., the value of the friction coefficient can be closely estimated.

Pressure loss

The pressure loss is a function of the coolant velocity, density, and the passage configuration. This loss may be determined from Fig. 11.9. Pressure losses may vary between 20 and 150 psi, depending on overall configuration, size of engine, and coolant used. Greater losses indicate need for redesign. Areas used for loss computation should be at operating temperatures. If room temperature passage areas are used, there will be a variation at operating conditions due to thermal expansion of the passage walls. Design should minimize pressure losses while maximizing heat transfer. Low velocities of the coolant fluid optimize pressure parameters but reduce heat transfer; hence a pragmatic solution that considers both will effect an operating compromise.

Tubing

Figure 11.9 may also be used for determining tubing pressure losses in the system. Excessive losses in tubing and elsewhere can result in too heavy a turbopump or other pressurizing unit. Tubing should be as short as possible, and consideration should be given to structures, system arrangement, and vibration.

Nozzle design

For further details of nozzle design, Chapter 5 may be used.

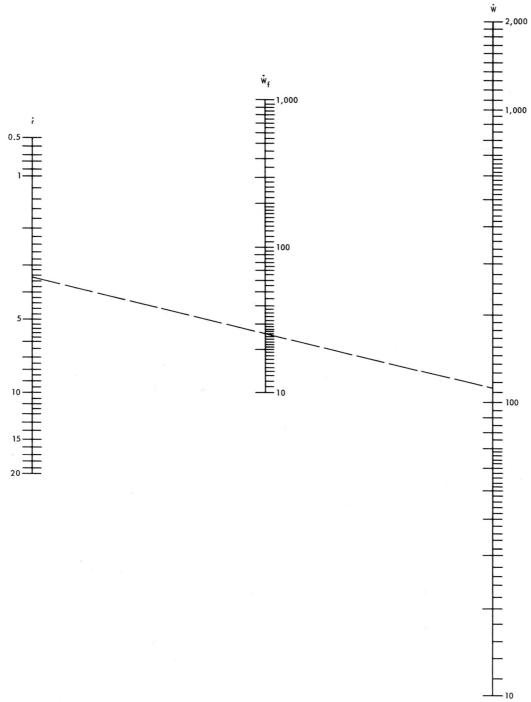

Fig. 11.4. Fuel-weight flow

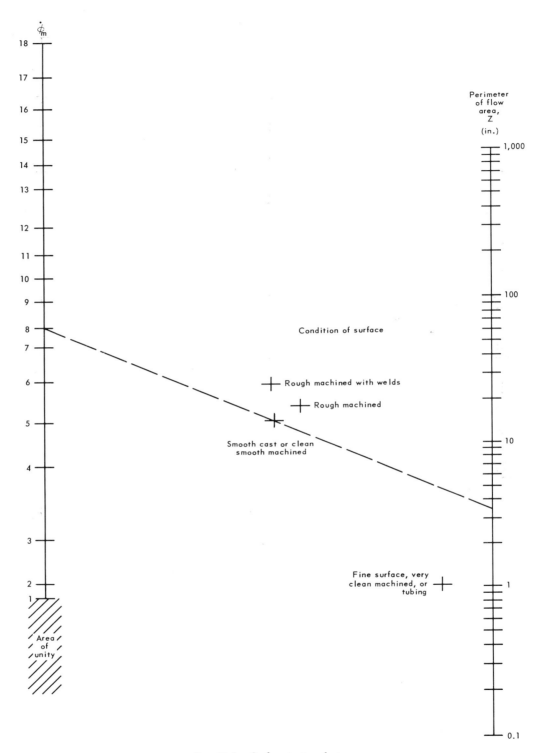

Fig. 11.5. Surface texture factor

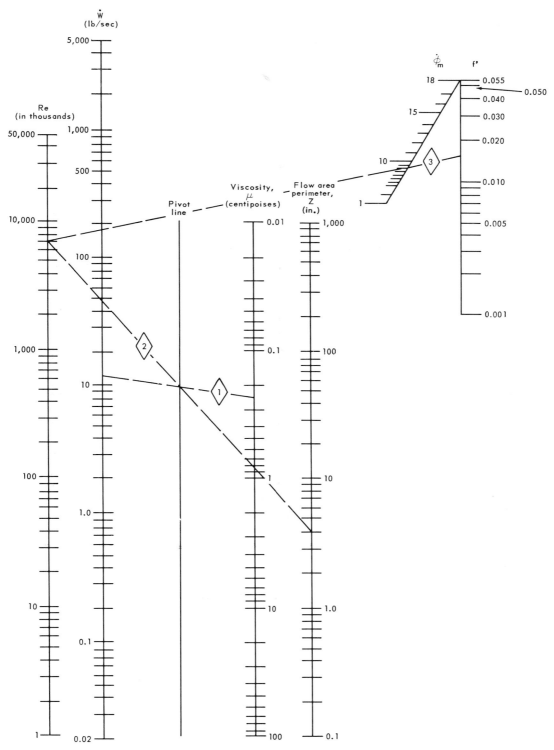

Fig. 11.6. Hydraulic friction loss (No. 1)

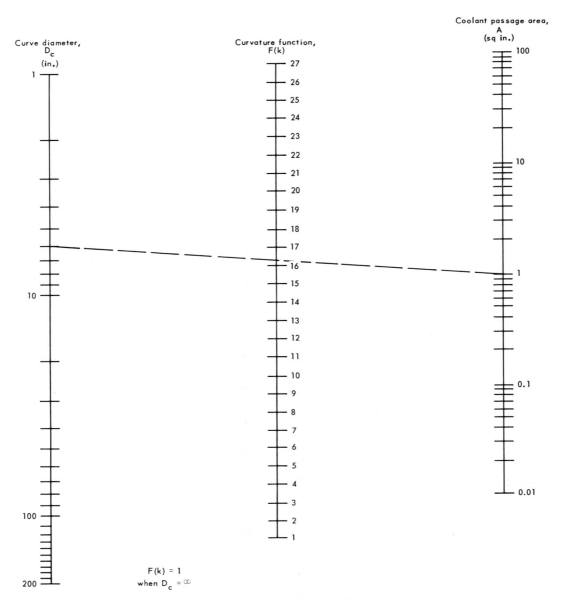

Fig. 11.7. Hydraulic friction loss (No. 2)

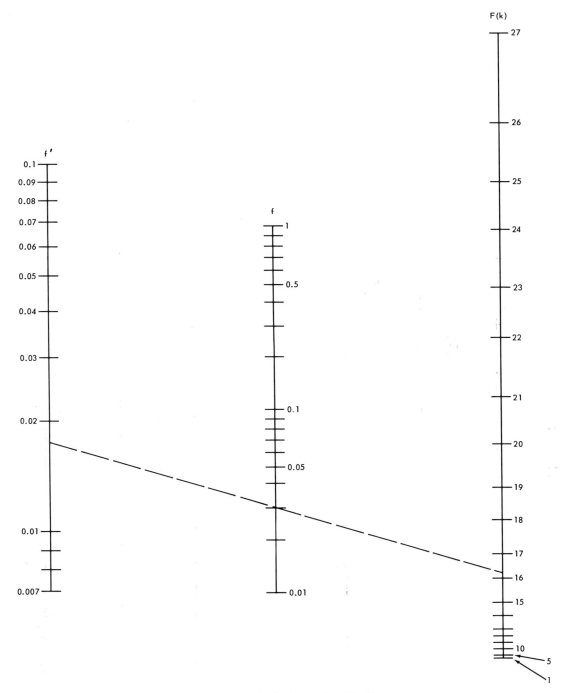

Fig. 11.8. Hydraulic friction loss (No. 3)

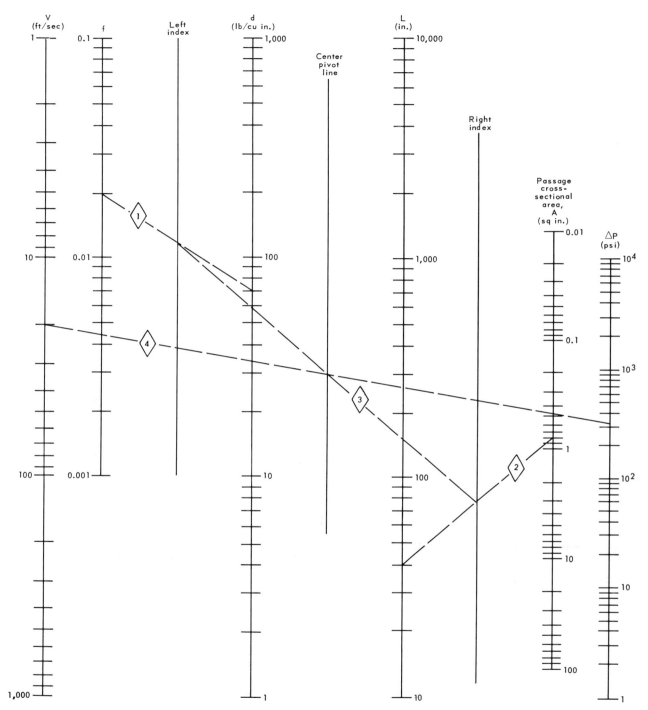

Fig. 11.9.   **Coolant friction pressure loss**

12

Pump and Turbine Design

Pump design

Liquid rocket engine pumps are usually of the centrifugal type. Piston and gear types when used with liquid oxygen or other liquified gases tend to trap the pumped fluid in enclosed pump spaces. Design nomographs in this chapter treat typical centrifugal pumps with radial, Francis, mixed flow, and axial impeller types. Pump performance, hence design, is based on the flow's being directly proportional to the pump speed, the head's being directly proportional to the square of the pump speed, and the power's being directly proportional to the cube of the pump speed.

Pump performance parameters basic to design are pump or shaft speed, flow, power, specific speed, suction specific speed, and pump head. The nomenclature for the design equations is as follows:

A = Flow area
d = Density
D = Impeller diameter
H = Head
$(H_s)_R$ = Required suction head
N = Shaft speed
N_s = Specific speed
P = Pressure (psi) or power (hp)
Q = Flow
S' = Suction specific speed
u = Impeller tip speed

V = Flow velocity
$\dot{W}$ = Weight flow
η_p = Pump efficiency
η_w = Weight merit factor
σ = Suction parameter
ψ = Impeller tip speed coefficient

The equation for the shaft specific speed is as follows:

$$N_s = 21.2N(Q^{1/2})/H^{3/4} \qquad (12\text{-}1)$$

where

$$H = u^2/\psi^2(2g) \qquad (12\text{-}2)$$

The flow can be defined in terms of area and respective flow velocity:

$$Q = AV \qquad (12\text{-}3)$$

The pump head is the total dynamic head; hence, it is the difference between pump discharge and pump suction head. The suction specific speed is as follows:

$$S' = N_s/\sigma^{3/4} = 21.2N(Q^{1/2})/(H_s)_R^{3/4} \qquad (12\text{-}4)$$

where

$$\sigma = (H_s)_R/H \qquad (12\text{-}5)$$

To illustrate the use of the nomographs in Figs. 12.1—12.8, the following example is used. Suppose a liquid oxygen pump is required that will deliver 90 lb/sec at a discharge pressure of 300 psi. The tank level is

135

5 ft above the pump. Oxygen tank pressurization is 35 psi. Frictional losses will be neglected.

1. From Fig. 12.1, using an oxygen density of 71.2 lb/cu ft, a weight flow of 90 lb/sec is equal to a flow of 1.38 cu ft/sec. This figure is obtained by connecting the $\dot{W}$ and d values with a straight edge to intersect the Q value on the centerline.

2. From Fig. 12.2, 300 psi equals a head of 600 ft. To convert 35 psi, enter it as 350 and reduce the resulting 700 to 70. Hence, 35 psi equals a head of 70 ft. The vapor pressure of liquid oxygen at its boiling point is 14.7 psi or 1 atm, equal to 29.8 ft. Therefore the available suction head above vapor pressure is 70 plus 5 minus 29.8, or 45.2 ft. The required suction head must be less than the available suction head. Using 80 per cent of the available figure gives a value of 36.16 ft. The available suction head (70 plus 5), when subtracted from the discharge head (600), gives the pump head: $600 - 75 = 525$ ft.

3. From Fig. 12.3, entering the above values for the pump head and required suction head, the suction parameter is read at 0.069.

4. From Fig. 12.4, estimating S' as about 7,500 (a conservative value), specific speed is read at 1,010. Where an estimation must be made, the guide line on the chart provides a method of first estimation.

5. In Fig. 12.5, entering the head value on line H and the specific speed on line N_s, a pivot point is established on the centerline. This point and the Q value is used to find a value of 4,500 rpm for N. This establishes the shaft speed. From the N_s line, it can be seen that the impeller is marginally of the Francis type.

6. From Fig. 12.6, using a constant of 1 for ψ, the impeller tip speed is established at 182 ft/sec. By entering this value in Fig.

12.7, the impeller diameter can be read as 9.2 in.

7. Pump efficiency can be established with Fig. 12.8 by entering the head on the outer right line and the weight flow on the outer left line to index a centerline pivot point. Using this point and the shaft horsepower, index the efficiency on the inner left line. The present example gives a value of 70 per cent for η_p. Horsepower values are obtained from the turbine power requirements (see Equation 12-7).

In rocket applications, weight is of prime importance. A figure of merit can be established for weight of individual pumps or total assemblies by means of Fig. 12.9.

The pump efficiency and weight merit factors must be considered in terms of the total application. A lightweight, inefficient pump may be more suitable for some installations whereas the converse may be true for others. Usually a compromise must be made.

Turbine design

Impulse turbines are preferred for liquid engine applications. Typical of these is the Curtis type velocity stage turbine. Design requirements like minimization of weight, maximization of efficiency, design simplification, and reliability must be considered in terms of such diverse parameters as power or pump output, duration of flight (including extension of service if the engine is to be used for more than one flight), vibration requirements in terms of the sources and resonances, and materials factors.

Light weight may be obtained by maximizing rim speed. There is an upper limit determined by allowable stress. If the rim speed is as high as possible and the rotor diameter as small as feasible, the over-all weight can be reduced to the minimum. An average range for rim speeds is between 500 and 1,300 ft/sec, depending on materials.

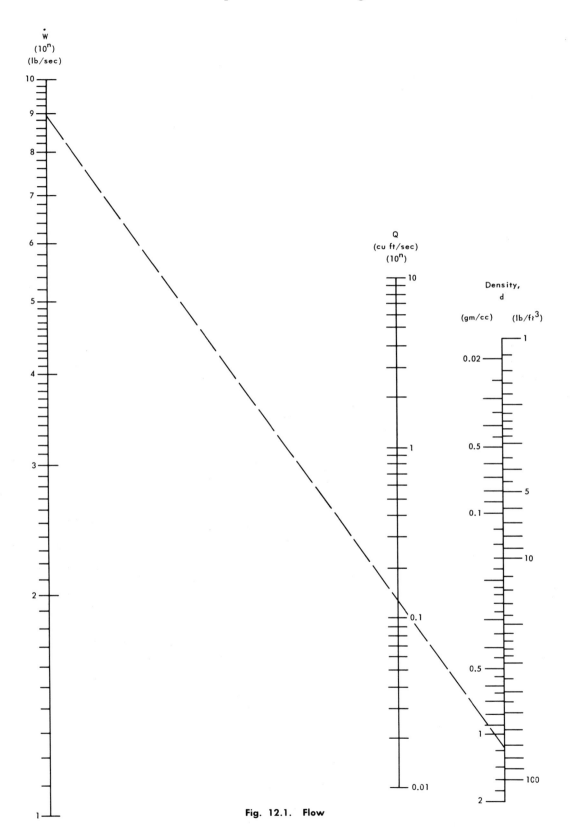

Fig. 12.1. Flow

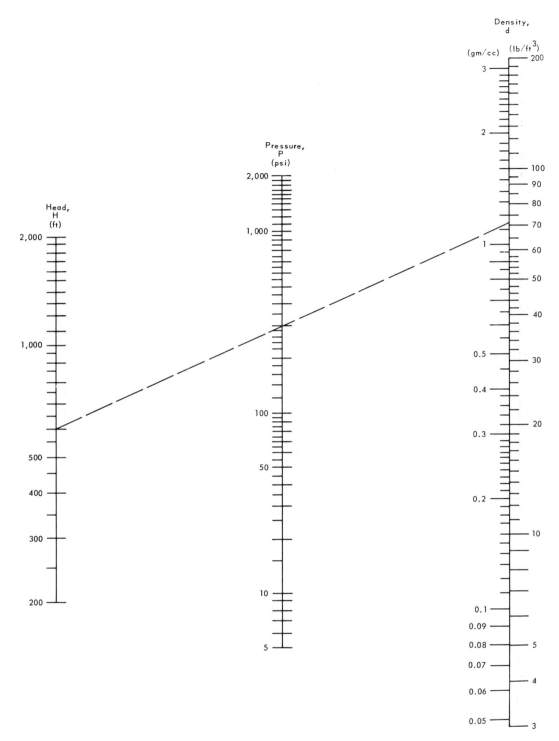

Fig. 12.2. Pressure head

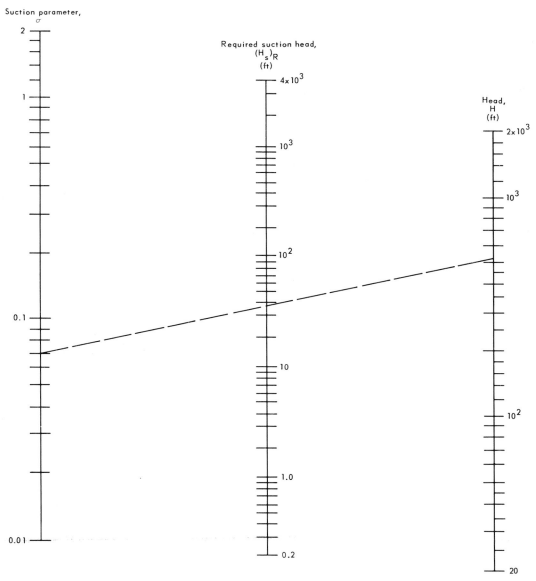

Fig. 12.3   Required suction head

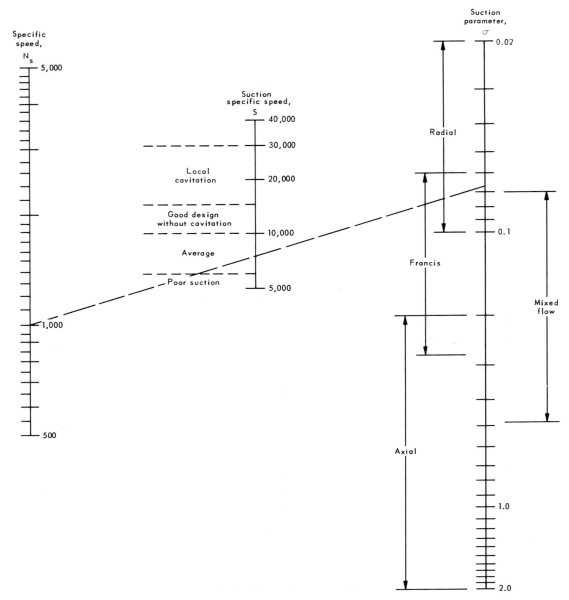

Fig. 12.4 Suction parameter

When specific suction speed is not previously determined, the suction parameter may be selected as indicated by the pump type and a value of specific suction speed selected in the average range in order to determine a preliminary specific speed for initial design purposes.

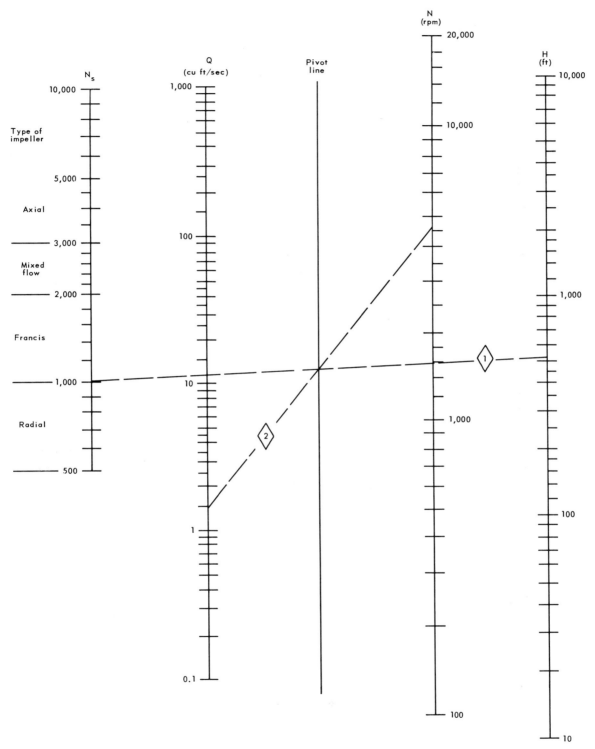

Fig. 12.5 Specific speed

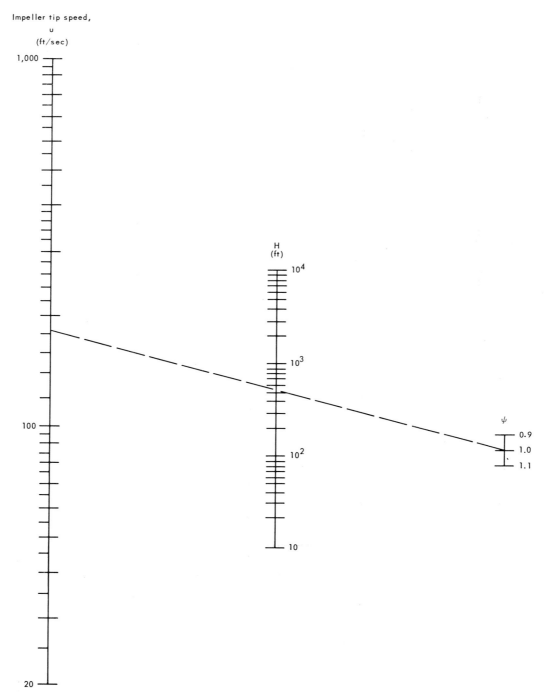

Fig. 12.6. Impeller tip speed

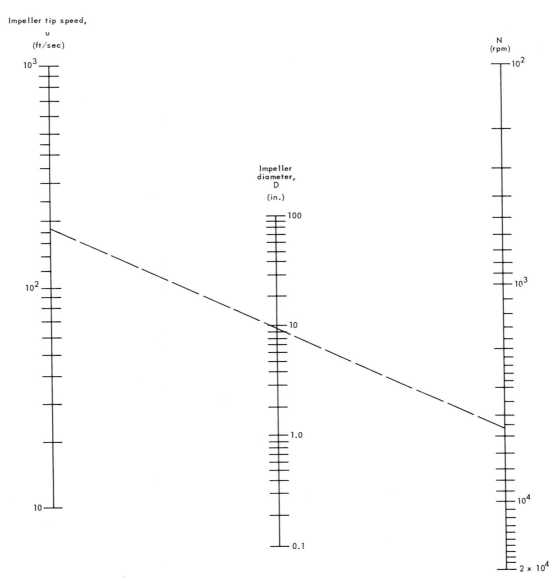

Fig. 12.7. Impeller diameter

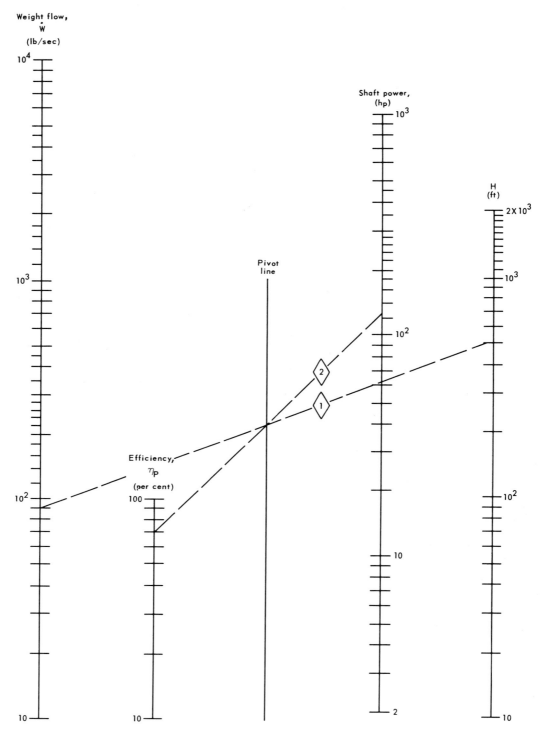

Fig. 12.8. Pump efficiency

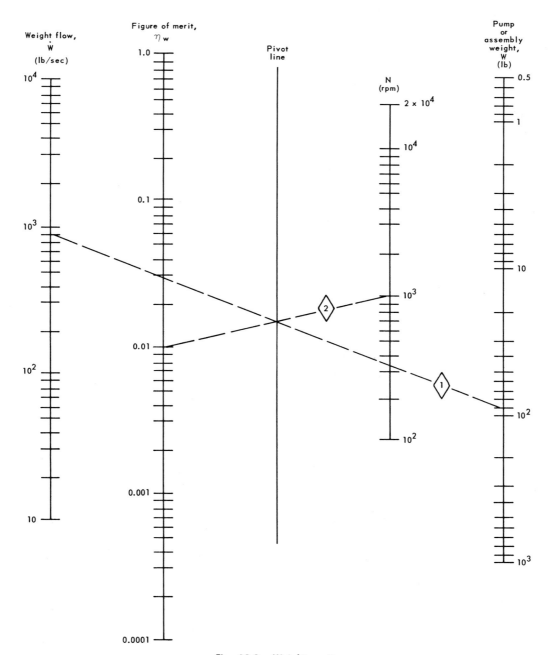

Fig. 12.9. Weight merit

Fig. 12.10 shows the upper limits of some materials in terms of rim speeds. If these limits are exceeded, tensile failure of the materials may result in total failure of the turbine. Many new materials are presently being tested to determine short and long period rim speed properties at various elevated temperatures.

Vibration can be most important in turbine design. All rocket applications must be tested for vibration. The turbine can be a source of vibration capable of affecting the entire system. Components of the system, in turn, can excite turbine resonance. Rotor operation, must be thoroughly considered in terms of the vibration spectrum of the combustion chamber.

Turbine power

The turbine power is equal to the sum of the pump power plus the power for any secondary units being driven (such as pumps or electrical generators) to supply servos or other auxiliaries. Figures 12.11 and 12.12 relate the parameters of efficiency, pressure, weight flow, and temperature, as follows:

$$\text{Shaft power} = \dot{W_t} C_p(\eta_t) T_1 [1 - (P_{ex}/P_1)^{(\gamma-1)/\gamma}]$$
$$= \Sigma \Delta P_n \dot{W}_n (d_n \eta_n)^{-1} \qquad (12\text{-}6)$$

where

$\dot{W_t}$ = flow through turbine
η_t = turbine efficiency
T_1 = nozzle inlet temperature
P_{ex} = turbine exhaust pressure
P_1 = turbine inlet pressure.

Subscript n indicates any component such as a pump, electric generator, or other piece of equipment.

Shaft power may also be estimated from the following:

$$\text{Shaft power} = \eta_t (H_1 - H_2) \dot{W} \qquad (12\text{-}7)$$

where $(H_1 - H_2)$ is the enthalpy drop. The efficiency η_t value may be as low as 0.40 or

higher than 0.70. The rated value for a specific turbine should be determined by test. Because shaft power is a direct function of inlet temperature, maximum temperatures are desirable but are obviously limited by blade materials.

Gas generator

The weight flow, $\dot{W_t}$, may be obtained by using a gas generator or tapping the combustion chamber. The gas generator may be either a solid charge or a liquid type generator. Figure 9.7 illustrated the liquid type generator which utilizes part of the propellant supply to supply pressure to the turbine. Figure 9.8 illustrated the gas tap arrangement. Monopropellant liquid generators such as a hydrogen peroxide gas unit may also be used. Inlet temperature limitations usually require cooling of the combustion

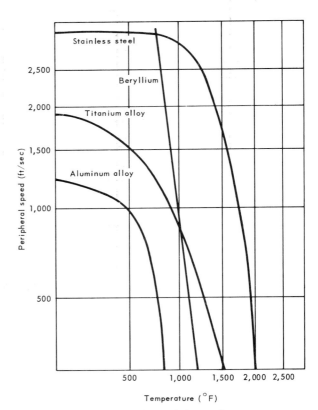

Fig. 12.10. Peripheral speed limits for some materials (diagrammatic only)

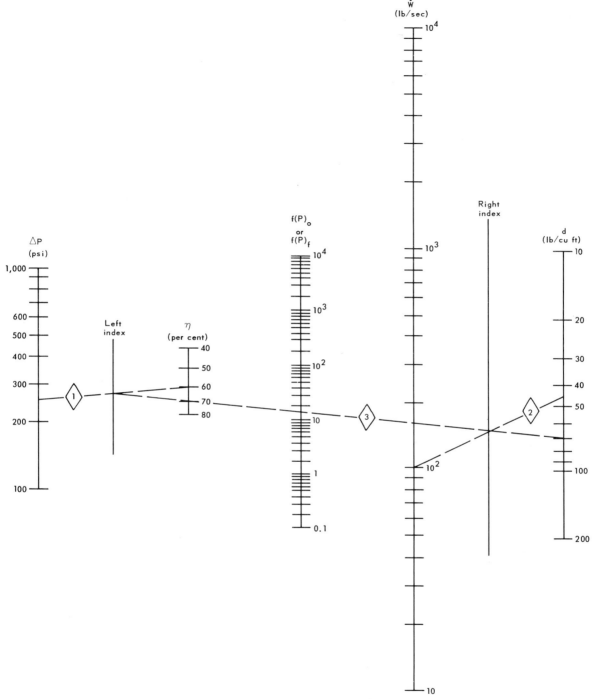

Fig. 12.11.   Pump turbine (No. 1)

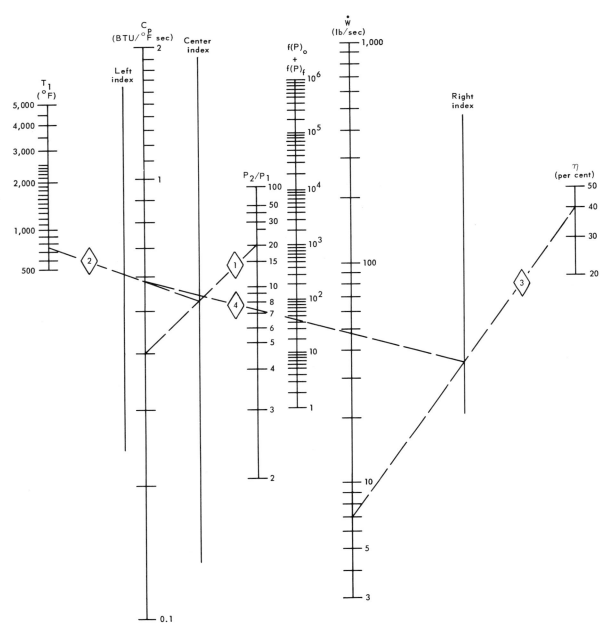

Fig. 12.12. Pump turbine (No. 2)

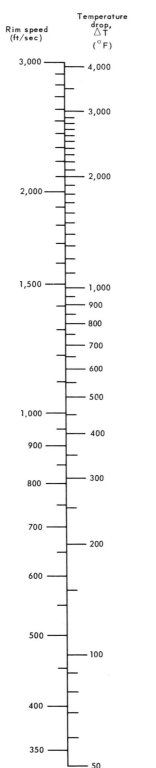

Fig. 12.13. Minimum turbine speed for all gases and all blade materials

gases before introduction into the turbine. Large rocket engines consume from 1 to 2 per cent of the total weight flow whereas smaller units (less than 9,500-lb thrust) may consume 2 to 5 per cent. Inlet pressure may be considered as a constant value.

Constant exit pressure may be established by use of a De Laval nozzle. The inlet/outlet pressure ratio will not vary with altitude; hence, turbine operation remains constant. Establishment of sonic throat conditions provides a level turbine outlet pressure curve.

Turbine blades

Weight, strength, shock, and vibration are major considerations in blade design. The peripheral speed is an important parameter which must be related to operating temperature and temperature drop. Figure 12.13 relates the minimum allowable rim speed to the temperature drop. Figure 12.10 relates the maximum speed due to stress for various materials to temperatures. Although these maximum speeds can be exceeded by using special alloys, the maximum for such special alloys must be predetermined by tests.

The stress is a function of blade length, blade density, and wheel diameter. A knowledge of the space requirements allows determination of blade length and wheel diameter.

Vibration in terms of rim speed, diameter of wheel, blade length, and blade width must be considered in terms of the resonance conditions in the turbopump and elsewhere in the system. Studies of system vibrations are discussed elsewhere in this text.

Initial operation shock is critical. Materials must withstand sudden exposure to hot gases and high pressures. The turbine drive gases usually enter the turbine at full-power operating conditions without any warm-up time. The materials therefore are exposed to high initiation shock.

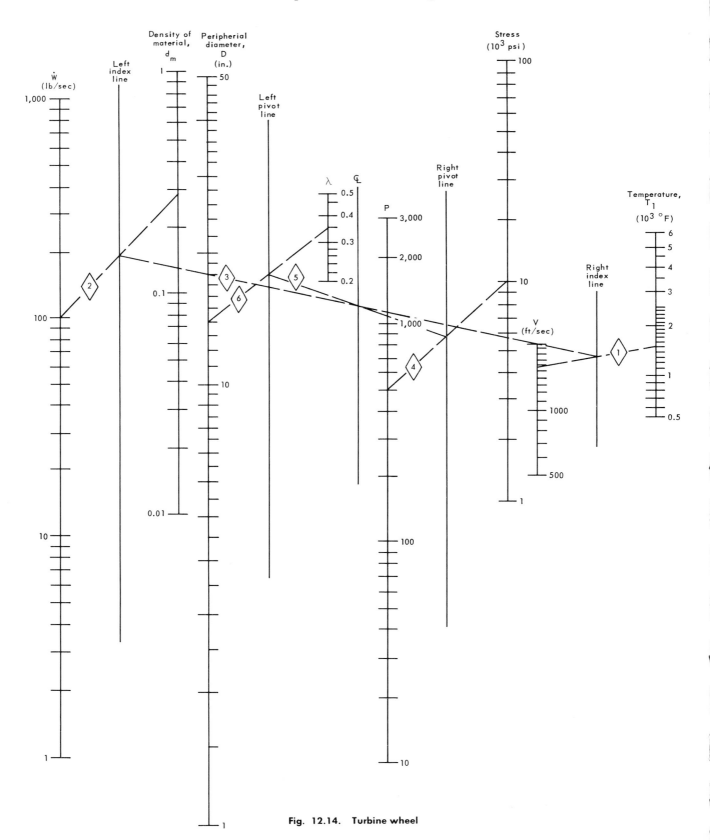

Fig. 12.14.   Turbine wheel

Wheel design

Turbine wheel peripheral diameter may be determined from Fig. 12.14 with a knowledge of the required weight flow, material density, rim speed, inlet temperature, gauging coefficient, inlet pressure, and allowable stress.

For optimization, the following equation may be utilized:

$$D = 1.96(\dot{W}V)^{1/2}(\lambda)^{-1/2}(d_m)^{1/2}(P_1)^{-1/2} \times$$
$$(T_1 + 459)^{1/2}S^{-1/2} \qquad (12\text{-}8)$$

where

D = turbine wheel peripheral diameter
$\dot{W}$ = weight flow through turbine
V = velocity
λ = gauging coefficient
d_m = density of material
S = allowable stress

The wheel diameter is limited by stress requirements, rim speeds, and operating temperatures. The basic wheel diameter equals the peripheral diameter minus the blade length:

$$D_{(basic)} = D - L \qquad (12\text{-}9)$$

Shaft diameter

The shaft diameter is a function of the torsional moment and the design shear stress,

$$D_{(shaft)} = 1.72\,(T_t)^{1/3}/S_{(shear)})^{1/3} \qquad (12\text{-}10)$$

and can be expressed in terms of horsepower and shaft speed:

$$D_{(shaft)} = 68.5(hp)^{1/3}(S_{(shear)})^{-1/3}(rpm)^{-1/3} \qquad (12\text{-}11)$$

The shaft diameter may also be determined directly from Fig. 12.15. If moment and torque are being considered, D_s may be determined from Fig. 12.16.

To optimize turbine efficiency, a higher speed may be desired than that made possible by direct coupling of pumps and turbine on a single shaft. Variation of pump-turbine speeds for such optimization may require gearing that will result in some weight penalty. Shaft design, gear configurations, valving, and other components, plus any auxiliary equipment, must be studied in terms of weight/power to reduce this index value to the lowest possible ratio. If a higher rate of rpm is indicated for turbines than for pumps, greater efficiency gearing may be in order. However, if the additional weight of gearing provides an actual lessening of optimal relationships, gearing should not be utilized.

Examples:

1. If the turbine inlet temperature is 1,500°F, the inlet pressure 500 psi, the temperature difference 900°F, the material density 0.28 lb/cu in., allowable stress 10,000 psi, weight flow 100 lb/sec, and gauging coefficient 0.35, what is the basic wheel diameter?

Selecting a rim velocity greater than 1,400 ft/sec (from Fig. 12.13) but less than 1,750 ft/sec (from Fig. 12.10), a near mean value of 1,550 is used for design. Entering this value and other parameters from the example in Fig. 12.14, the wheel diameter, D, is established at 13.8 in. Using this value, plus other parameters, in Fig. 12.17, the blade length, L, is established at 0.274 in. Therefore, for this relationship, the basic diameter is: $D - L = 13.8 - 0.274 = 13.526$ in.

2. What is the design shaft diameter if the allowable stress is 50,000 psi with 3,900 rpm and 275 hp?

From Fig. 12.15, the diameter of the shaft is 0.76 in.

3. What is the weight flow of the turbine if the following conditions hold:

a. The turbine inlet temperature is 750°F; C_p is 0.40 Btu/°F sec; the P_2/P_1 ratio is 22; and η equals 40 per cent.

b. The oxidizer pump delivers a weight flow of 100 lb/sec at a pressure of 250 psi, the density of the oxidizer being 45 lb/cu ft, with an η of 60 per cent.

c. The fuel pump delivers a weight flow of 150 lb/sec, a pressure difference of 355 psi, a density of 50 lb/cu ft with an η of 60 per cent.

Entering the oxidizer values in Fig. 12.11, $f(P)_o$ is read as 15.

Entering the fuel values in Fig. 12.11, $f(P)_f$ is read as 28.

The value of $f(P)_o + f(P)_f$ equal to 43 is entered into Fig. 12.12 with the other turbine parameters to read the weight flow at 6.8 lb/sec.

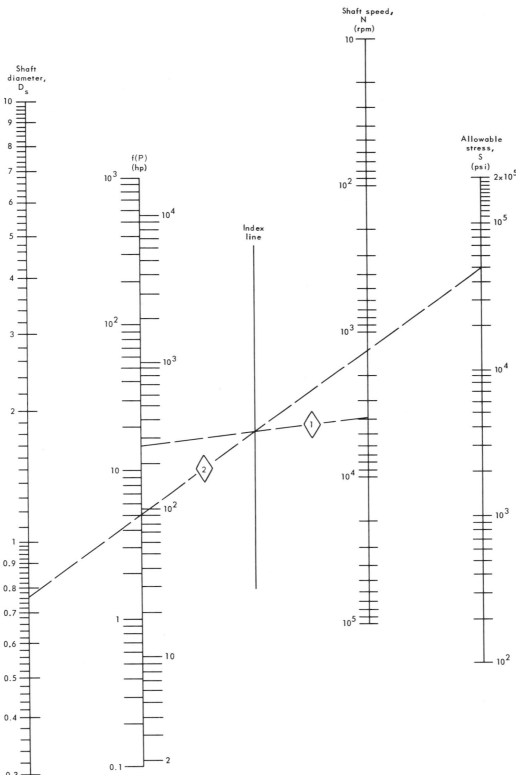

Fig. 12.15. Shaft diameter

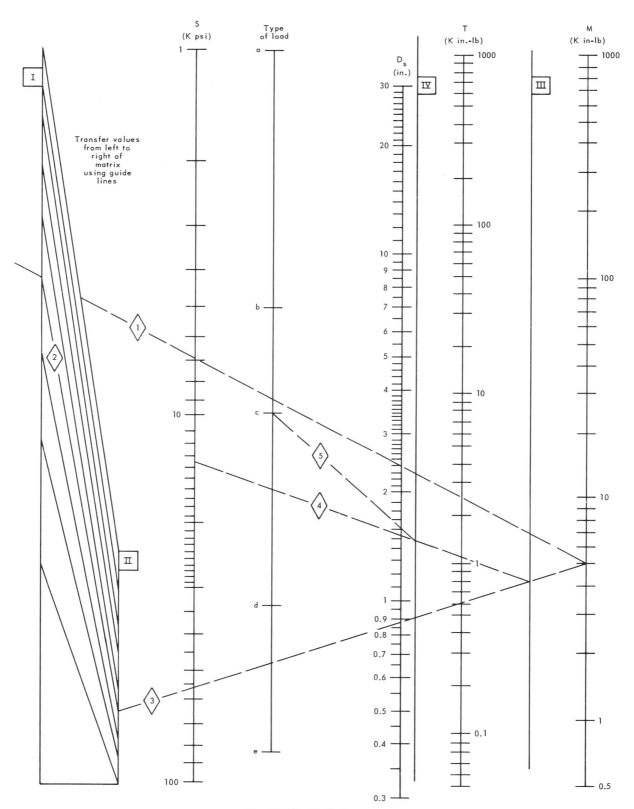

Fig. 12.16.   Shaft diameter

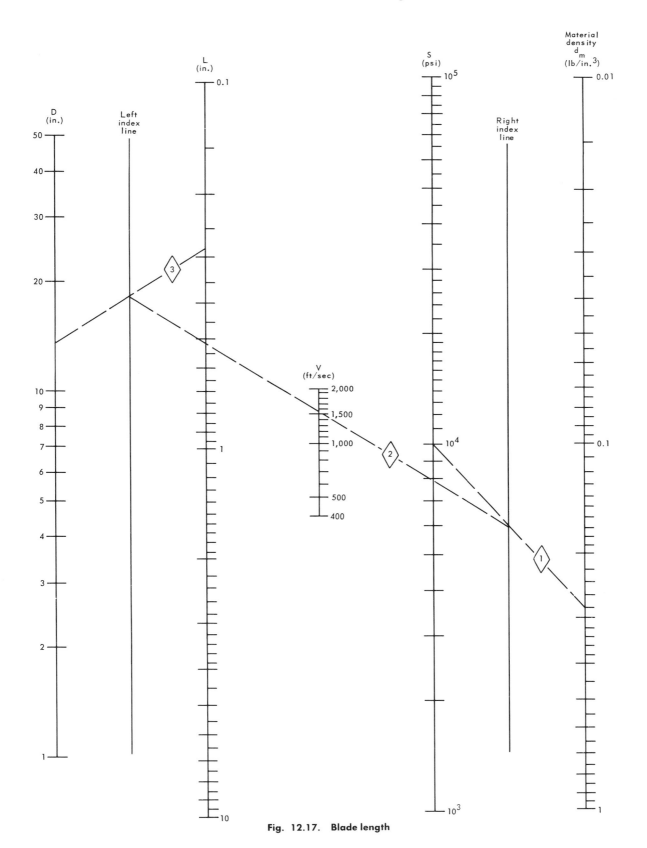

Fig. 12.17.   Blade length

13

Injector Design

The injector is a device designed to accept the propellant and inject it into the combustion chamber. Its functions include directing and mixing or atomizing the fluids. Mixing may be accomplished by impingement, chamber turbulence, spray and vaporization within intersecting patterns, or by mixing before injection.

Impingement devices like the injector shown in Fig. 13.1 are suitable for self-igniting propellants as well as others. With oxidizer impinging upon fuel, heat generation vaporizes the fluids so that the reaction proceeds in the gas phase. Dissimilar impinging streams have been most successful for many engines.

Nonimpinging spray or vaporizing streams usually initiate reaction in the vapor phase. Premixing devices such as that illustrated in Fig. 13.2 are suitable for nonhypergolic propellants but are not advisable for hypergolic (that is, self-igniting) mixtures. The oxidizer and fuel are combined in the injector chamber prior to combustion chamber injection.

Injectors with built-in valves provide greater control of flow, mixture ratio, and other injector functions. Figure 13.3 illustrates a typical injector with valve. This type of device provides a method of varying thrust.

Injectors may be considered as a shell or plate with many orifices (or equivalent slots) for propellant passage. Basic injector orifice types are illustrated in Fig. 13.4. Each configuration has a flow coefficient associated with it in terms of its shape and size as indicated in Fig. 13.5. With a knowledge of the flow coefficient, the size of the orifice area with regard to specified pressure drop can be determined from Fig. 13.6. After determining the orifice area, Fig. 13.7 may be utilized to determine the velocity of the fluids. The velocity must be great enough to insure proper entry of the propellant into the combustion chamber. Impingement devices must have sufficient momentum to guarantee proper impingement.

The basic injector design equations are:

$$V = 0.08333\dot{W}/nAd = 0.1177C_d d^{-1/2}(\Delta P)^{1/2}$$

$$\tag{13-1}$$

$$A = 0.706\dot{W}/C_d d^{1/2}(\Delta P)^{1/2}n \tag{13-2}$$

Examples:

1. Using a group of 10 sharp-edged orifices with a design pressure drop of 100 psi, an oxidizer having a density of 71.2 lb/cu in and a weight flow of 90 lb/sec, what is the orifice area?

The sharp-edge orifice is illustrated on the extreme right in Fig. 13.4. From Fig.

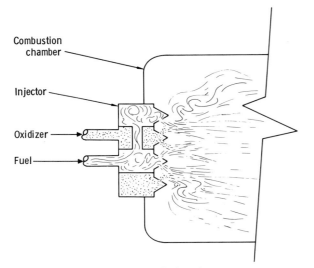

Fig. 13.1. Impinging fuel-oxidizer injector

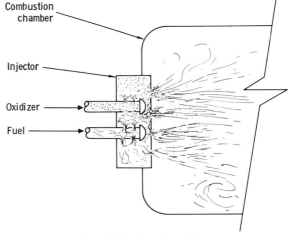

13.5, C_d for this configuration is about 0.615.

Using this value and the other parameters in Fig. 13.6, the answer is 0.0128 sq in.

2. What is the velocity for this configuration? Entering these values into Fig. 13.7, the velocity is 0.87 ft/sec.

If the selected orifice size is too small, it may become plugged during operation, usually by foreign matter, thus leading to injector malfunction. However, if orifice size is too great, atomization and mixing

Fig. 13.2. Premix injector

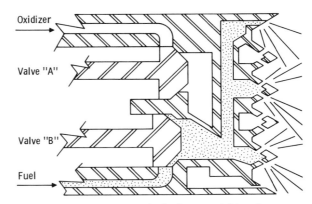

Fig. 13.3 Injector with "built-in" variable valves
Oxidizer valve, A, shown closed; fuel valve, B, shown open.

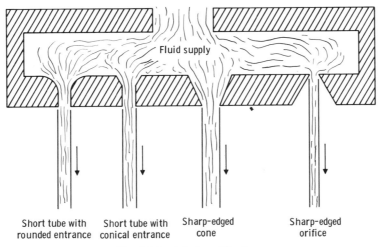

Short tube with rounded entrance | Short tube with conical entrance | Sharp-edged cone | Sharp-edged orifice

Fig. 13.4. Injector orifice types

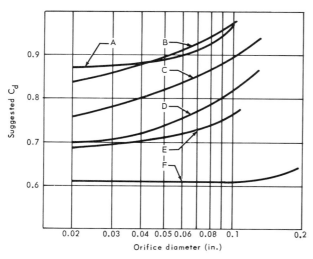

Fig. 13.5. Suggested design flow coefficients for injector orifices of typical configurations

A—short tube with rounded entrance (L/D) ~ 5)
B—short tube with rounded entrance (L/D) ~ 3)
C—short tube with conical entrance (L/D) ~ .7)
D—general short tube with conical entrance
E—sharp-edged cone
F—sharp-edged orifice

will be incomplete. Typical sizes are about 0.06 to 0.13 in.

Stress

Pressure difference is at a maximum prior to the establishment of rated chamber pressure, the pressure difference at the maximum being the chamber pressure (rated), plus the rated pressure drop.

$$P_{(max.)} = P_c + \Delta P \qquad (13\text{-}3)$$

Shock and this initial pressure maximum may produce the greatest plate stress. Since failure may occur more rapidly at elevated operating temperatures, however, both areas of operation must be studied.

Vibration parameters of the injector plate may be estimated by use of nomographs in the vibration section of this text. Vibration of the injector plate can result in erratic combustion, shock, and possible failure of injectors and other system components. Characteristic resonance of injector plates is obviously important in such design.

The injector plate is not exposed to the full flame temperature because of insulating characteristics of the injected vapors and also because of the downstream position of the flame front. These conditions often lead to better operation than expected, in terms of stress, when flame temperature is used as that temperature to which the injector plate will be exposed. Heat transfer must be considered in injector design.

Expansion of the injection holes increases the effective area at operating temperatures and must be considered in terms of the rated operation. If it is not accounted for, operation may differ from design beyond allowable limits.

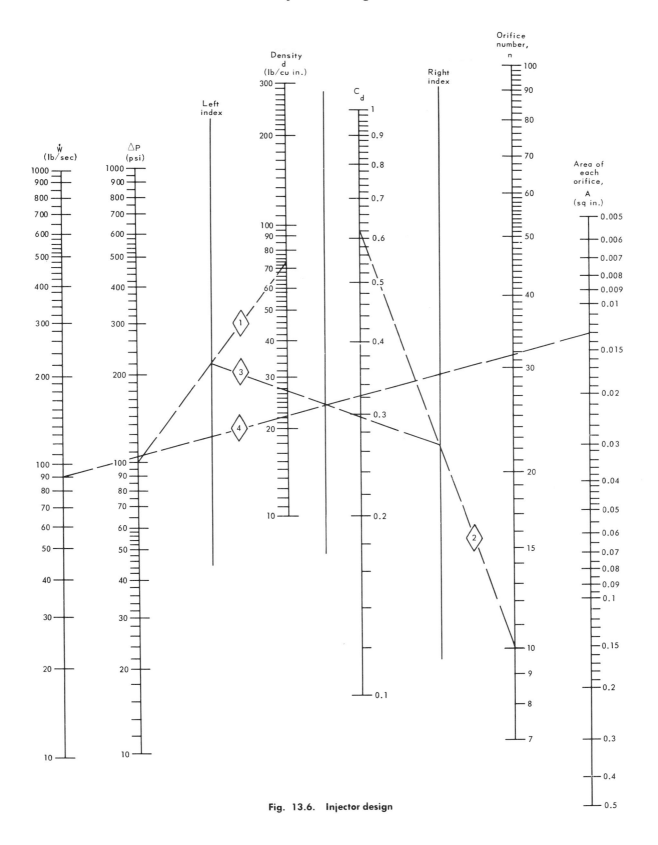

Fig. 13.6. Injector design

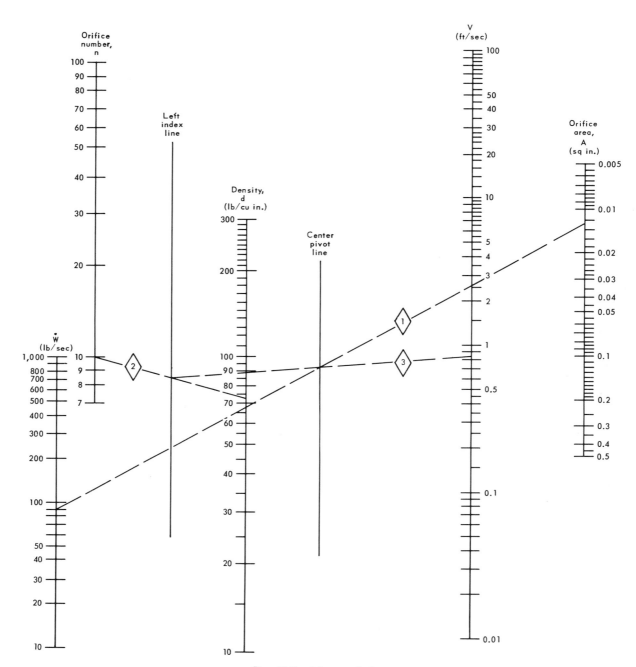

Fig. 13.7. Injector velocity

14

Heat Transfer and Thermal Stress

Heat transfer considerations are of vital importance in all phases of chemical rocket design. Conditions at the nozzle throat may maximize heat transfer. Injector plates and other units exposed to combustion gas must be able to resist the heat. Design of cooled nozzles (both liquid and solid) and combustion chambers depends upon a knowledge of the parameters of heat transfer.

Basically, there are three areas of major interest:

1. Transfer from a gas to a wall.

2. Transfer through material of wall from one face to another face.

3. Transfer from wall to coolant, either liquid or solid.

The total heat transferred can be computed from the standard equation:

$$Q = Aq \qquad (14\text{-}1)$$

where

Q = total heat transferred per unit time
q = heat transferred per unit area
A = area for heat transfer.

The heat transferred per unit area can be determined from:

$$q = h_t \Delta T \qquad (14\text{-}2)$$

where

h_t = total heat transfer coefficient
Δt = temperature gradient at the point of interest, that is, the temperature difference $(T_1 - T_2)$ in the Newton rate equation.

These relationships are illustrated in Fig. 14.1.

Heat transferred from combustion gas

Combustion products are generally in turbulent flow. The boundary flow is a function of the flow diameter and the Reynolds number. Figure 14.2 illustrates the laminar and turbulent relationships.

The exact nature of the flow depends on the Reynolds number, the gas temperature, the pressure, the reaction process, and other environmental conditions. The heat transfer will therefore be a function of the basic parameters established by the conditions of the gas, the passage, and the flow.

The heat transfer coefficient, h_c, may be described in terms of three fundamental gas parameters—the Nusselt number, Nu; the Prandtl number, Pr; and the Reynolds number, Re:

$$h_c = \text{Nu}(k/D) \qquad (14\text{-}3)$$

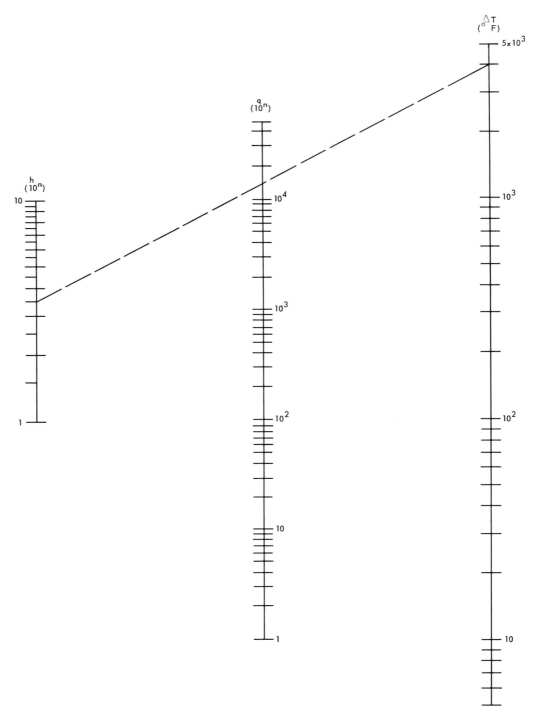

Fig. 14.1. Heat transferred per unit area

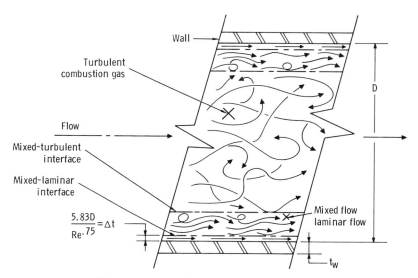

Fig. 14.2. Basic flows of combustion products

where

D = hydraulic diameter obtained from Fig. 14.3

k = gas thermal conductivity.

The Nusselt number and, consequently, h_c, for cylinders and tubes (and combustion chambers and nozzles) can be determined from the following relationship:

$$\text{Nu} = 0.023(\text{Re})^{0.8}(\text{Pr})^{0.33} \qquad (14\text{-}4)$$

where the constant 0.023 applies to combustion chamber type turbulence.

For rocket gas at combustion temperatures

$$h_c \cong 0.0176(k/D)(\text{Re})^{0.8} \qquad (14\text{-}5)$$

The Reynolds number depends upon the density and viscosity of the gas, the gas velocity, and the diameter of the passage. The exact value of this number may be determined from Fig. 14.4 or the following equation:

$$\text{Re} = VDd/\mu \qquad (14\text{-}6)$$

where

V = velocity
d = gas density
μ = viscosity.

The Prandtl number of the fluid at elevated temperatures may be determined from Fig. 14.5 and 14.6. For coolant and gases, this number can be defined in terms of thermal conductivity, heat capacity at constant pressure, and viscosity, in the following relationship:

$$\text{Pr} = \mu C_p/k \qquad (14\text{-}7)$$

To determine the gas heat transfer coefficient, h_c, the following steps should be followed:

1. From Fig. 14.4 estimate the Reynolds number.

2. From Fig. 14.7 estimate the heat transfer coefficient.

It is also possible to approximate h_c from Fig. 14.8.

Mass velocity

The mass velocity, G, is commonly used in heat transfer and fluid flow. By defining the mass velocity as follows,

$$G = Vd = \dot{W}/A \qquad (14\text{-}8)$$

a constant product of the free stream velocity

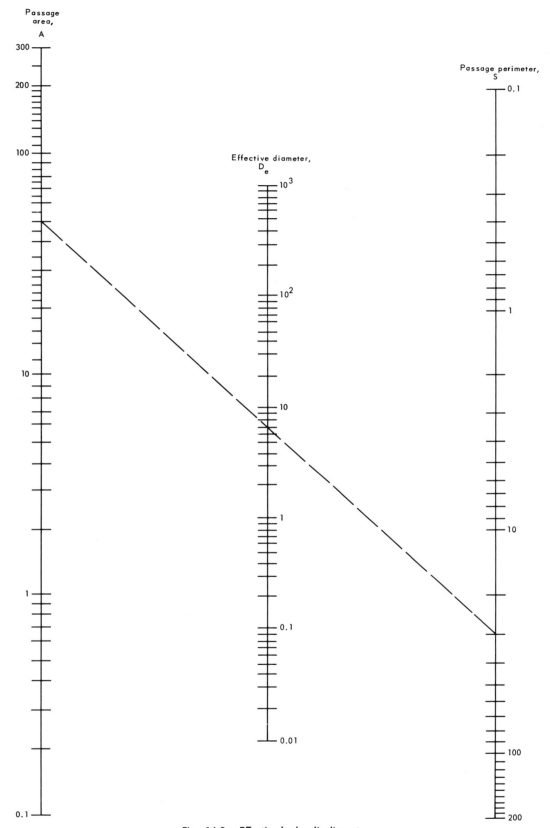

Fig. 14.3. Effective hydraulic diameter

164

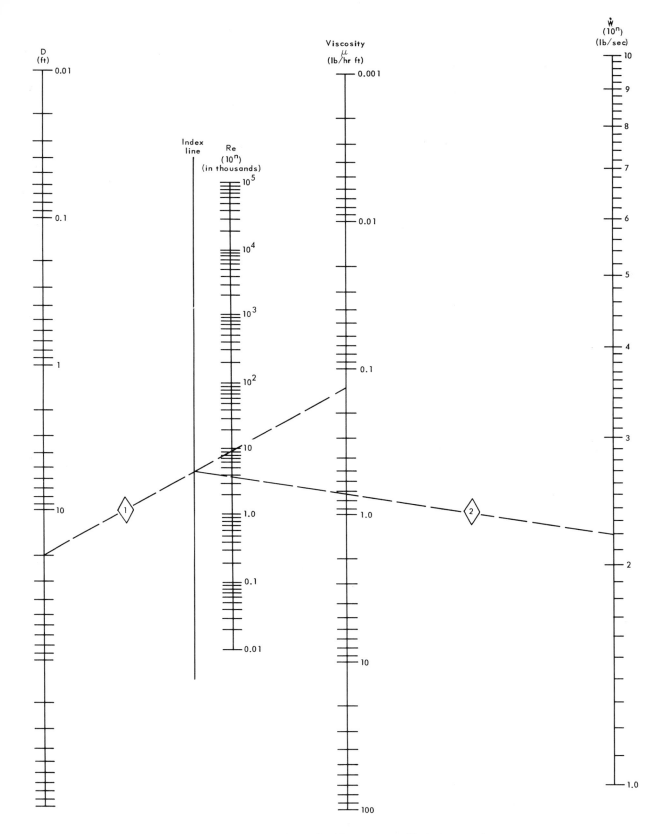

Fig. 14.4 Reynolds number (for circular or elliptical passage)

165

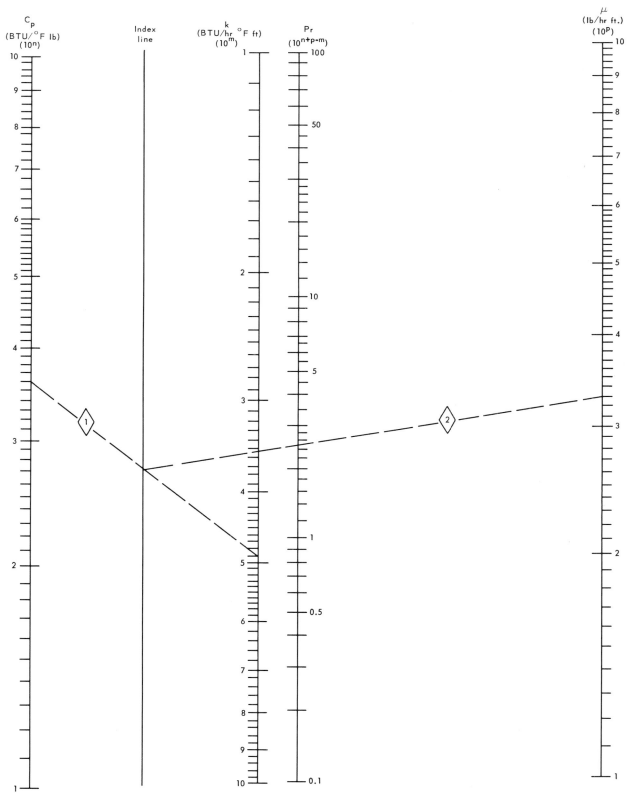

Fig. 14.5. Prandtl number

and density is achieved. This can be developed from the equation for flow continuity,

$$\dot{m}v = AV = \text{constant} \qquad (14\text{-}9)$$

where v is the specific volume.

The heat transfer coefficient may therefore be expressed as

$$h_c = CG^{0.8}D^{0.2} \qquad (14\text{-}10)$$

where C may be determined experimentally or from the formula

$$C = 0.023(\text{Pr})^{1/3}k/\mu^{0.8} \qquad (14\text{-}11)$$

By arranging the terms in the Nusselt equation, a group may be defined as

$$J = h(\text{Pr})^{2/3}/VC_pd = h(C_pG)^{-1}(\text{Pr})^{2/3} \qquad (14\text{-}12)$$

This can be related directly to a function of the Reynolds number.

Radiation coefficient

The total heat transfer coefficient is the sum of the convective and radiative coefficients.

$$h_t = h_c + h_r \qquad (14\text{-}13)$$

The total heat transfer coefficient may be expressed as a function of the convective coefficient as in Fig. 14.9. This graph can be used to determine the value of h_t, the total heat transfer coefficient including radiation. Radiation transfer is comparatively minor and is often not computed in rocket design.

Heat transferred through walls

The equivalent heat transfer coefficient, h_w, may be deduced directly in terms of the wall thickness and the heat conduction of the wall material as follows:

$$h_w = k/t_w \qquad (14\text{-}14)$$

The thermal conductivity of the material at operating temperatures and the wall thickness may be entered into Fig. 14.10 to esti-

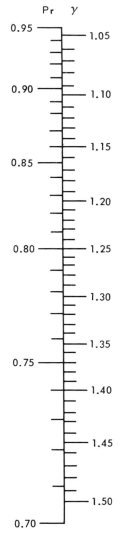

Fig. 14.6. Prandtl number at combustion temperature

mate the wall equivalent heat transfer coefficient.

With a knowledge of the coefficient, the heat transferred, and the temperature of one face, the temperature of the other face can be estimated by

$$T_x = T_o + q/h_w = T_o + \frac{h_w}{h_o}(\Delta T_w) \qquad (14\text{-}15)$$

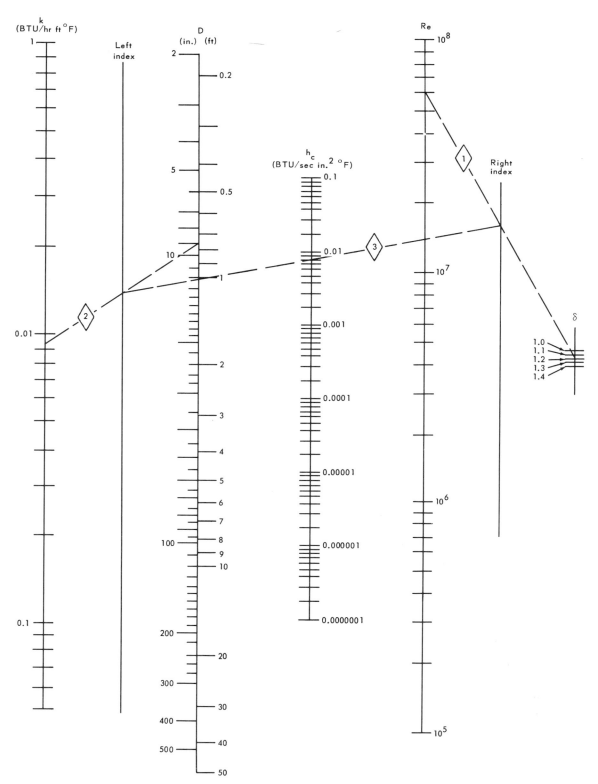

Fig. 14.7. Combustion gas heat transfer coefficient

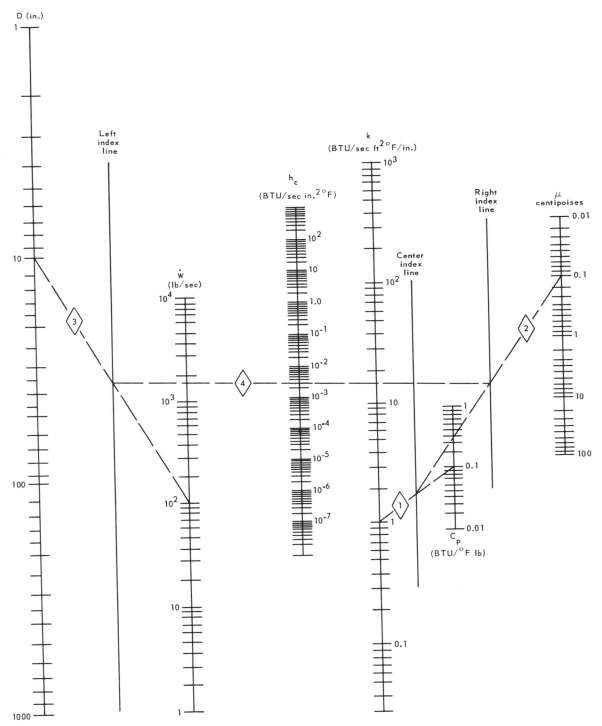

Fig. 14.8. Heat transfer convection coefficient

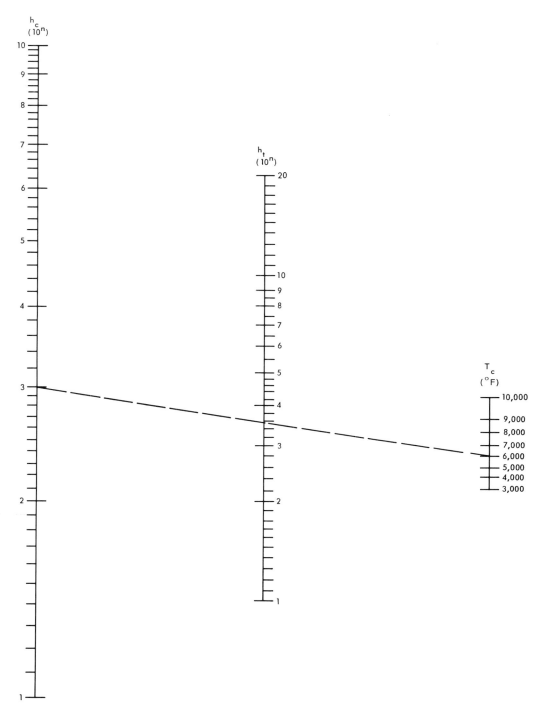

Fig. 14.9. Radiation compensation

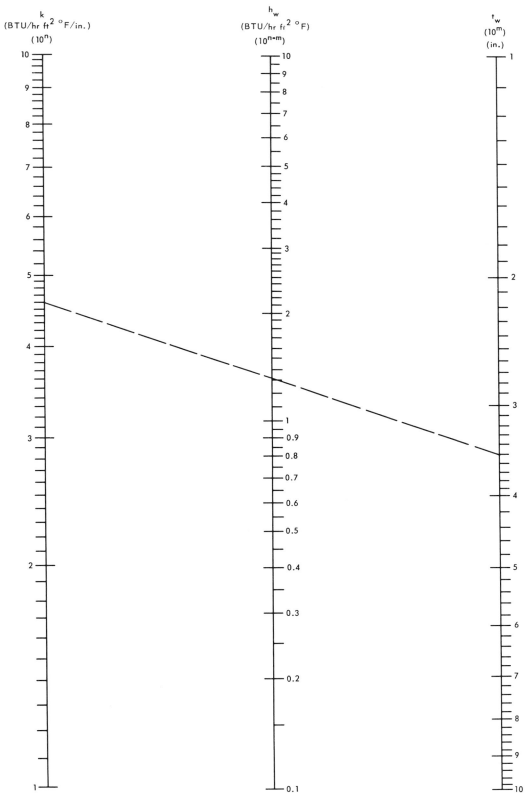

Fig. 14.10. **Wall equivalent heat transfer coefficient,** h_w

Heat transferred to coolant

The liquid heat transfer coefficient, h_o, can be defined in terms of the Reynolds and the Prandtl numbers of the coolant as follows:

$$h_o = 0.023 \dot{W} C_p / A (\text{Pr})^{2/3} (\text{Re})^{1/5} \quad (14\text{-}16)$$

This formulation defines the h_t coefficient for liquids in Equation 14-2. The value of this coefficient can be estimated directly from Fig. 14.11. This figure is similar to Fig. 14.8 but with Pr and Re as parameters instead of the basic properties, k, μ, and C_p.

If the boiling point of the coolant is exceeded by the wall temperature, the following formulation gives the increase in the effective heat transfer coefficient

$$h_t = h_o [1 + 0.01 (T_w - T_b)] \quad (14\text{-}17)$$

where

T_w = wall temperature
T_b = boiling point.

This formula is effective at wall temperatures exceeding the boiling point by 1 to 100°F. Where the wall temperature is less than the boiling point, $h_t = h_o$. However, if the coolant is totally converted to a gas, the standard liquid to gas state formulations apply.

The coolant temperature rise can be computed from the following formula:

$$\Delta T = A q / \dot{W} C_p \quad (14\text{-}18)$$

The temperature rise must not be large for most designs. The temperature rise should not generally permit boiling of the liquid. Figure 14.12 may be utilized to determine this temperature rise. In long passages, such as a regenerative coolant passage, q varies from point to point, being highest at or near the throat. For such cases, a repetitive incremental technique can be used, with an average q for each increment.

Thermal stress

Liquid rocket engine chambers and nozzles are exposed to combustion products in the temperature range of 4,000 to 9,000° F. Cooling of the chamber and nozzle results in extreme temperature differences of exposed to hot gases in the range of 3,000 to 7,000°F. Thermal stress therefore is a paramount problem.

In the design of rockets, stress studies as well as the more obvious thermal limit studies must be made to determine temperature limits. Some materials which appear to offer optimum high temperature characteristics fail to meet the thermal stress requirements.

The following equation gives the thermal stress for cylinders:

$$s_t = 2R^2 E \Delta T \Delta \alpha / [(1 - 2v)R^2 + R_i^2] \quad (14\text{-}19)$$

where

ΔT = change in temperature (°F)
$\Delta \alpha$ = difference between coefficients of thermal expansion of propellant and chamber
v = Poisson's ratio
E = modulus of elasticity of propellant
R_i = inner radius of grain
R = chamber radius
S_t = thermal stress

Thermal expansion characteristics of the chamber wall exposed to hot gases at the inner surface result in forces which produce a compressive stress at the inner face and a tensile stress at the outer face. Calculations to determine maximum values of these stresses are simplified by Fig. 14.13.

Application of Fig. 14.13 to rocket chambers and nozzles can reveal stresses above the yield point of the materials utilized in construction.

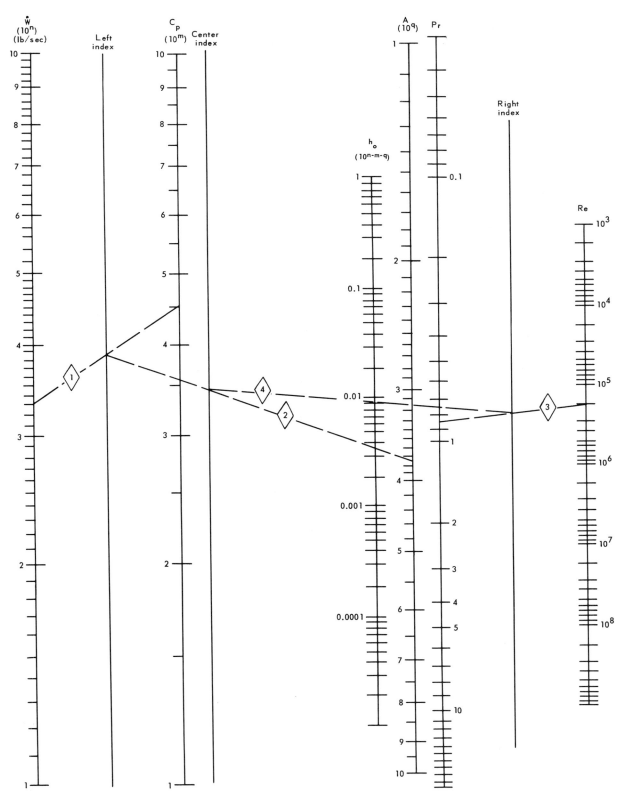

Fig. 14.11. Coolant heat transfer coefficient

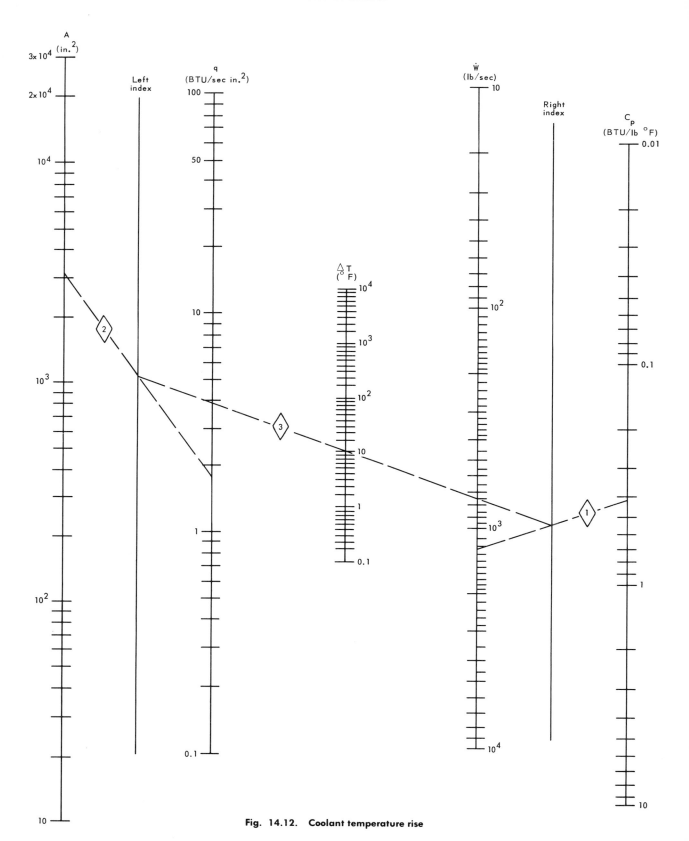

Fig. 14.12. Coolant temperature rise

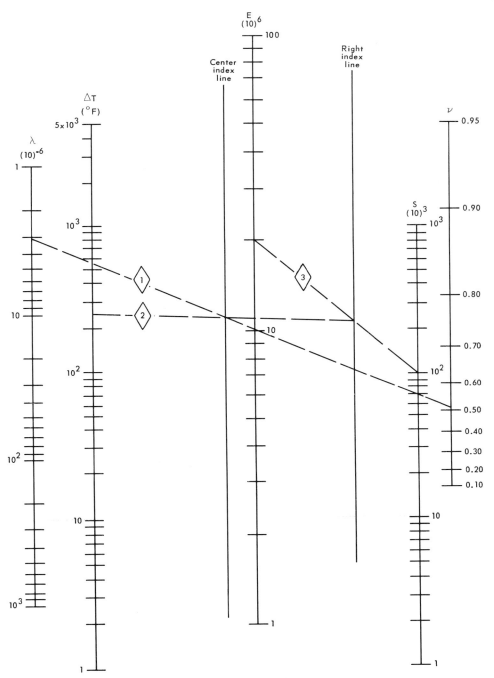

Fig. 14.13. Thermal stress

λ = *gaging coefficient derived from configuration or test.   This graph may be used for chambers,*
nozzles, tanks, cases, and all internally burning solid propellant grains.

15

Systems Vibration

Systems vibration is an important consideration in liquid and solid rocket design. In solid rockets, "the system" in vibration consists of the motor, inclusive of case, nozzle, and grain. In liquid engine design, the total system inclusive of combustion chamber, nozzle, turbine, pumps, tanks, etc., must be studied in terms of resonance.

Resonance of one component can lead to malfunction of a different component. Storage tank resonance, perhaps excited by turbine or pumps, can lead to surging in the supply lines, which in turn can result in faulty combustion. Figure 15.1 illustrates the general nomenclature that may be utilized in vibration studies. Vibration resonance of each component may exist in several forms. For example, vibration in the chamber area can exist in the combustion space in a lengthwise mode or a 'sloshing' mode or in the metal of the chamber itself either from injector to nozzle or ringwise.

Combustion products

Vibration of combustion products can be divided into two general regions, the low-frequency, or chugging, type and the high-frequency type. The chugging type, usually considered below 100 cycles per second, may be considered in terms of propellant flow and related parameters. The high-frequency type is more complex. These high-frequency vibrations are directly coupled to the natural frequencies of the combustion chamber.

The chugging type is often observed at initiation or cut-off of the engine. Chugging can result in resonance throughout the vehicle. Delicate electronics in the guidance section may be damaged by violent shaking. Specific impulse often falls to a fraction of expected values. The chamber can be ripped open by sudden increases in combustion pressure. Attachments and supports can be shaken free. Such oscillations cause these physically obvious malfunctions and also a number of less noticeable adverse conditions.

The chamber oscillation wave in low-frequency vibration can be studied in terms of the weight-flow-pressure relationships. The pressure in the wave front is greater than that in the surrounding medium. Due to increased speed of reaction in the wave front, the effective pressure behind the wave drops. When the moving high-pressure region reaches the injector plate, the weight flow decreases as a function of the propellant pressure drop across the plate. The variation of weight flow is related as follows:

$$W_x = \dot{W}(P_x - P_p)^{1/2}(P_c - P_p)^{1/2} \qquad (15\text{-}1)$$

176

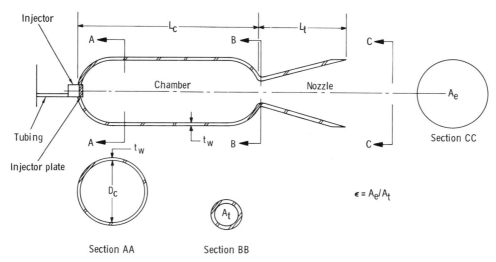

Fig. 15.1. **Combustion chamber and nozzle for vibration analysis**

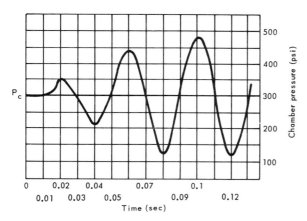

Fig. 15.2. **Low-frequency resonance pressure variation of 300-psi liquid rocket combustion chamber**

where

P_c = chamber pressure
P_p = propellant pressure
P_x = wave instantaneous pressure.

A time delay is required for this flow to become effective. In this time lag, the high-
pressure region passes and is followed by the
low-pressure region. During the high-pressure period ($P_x > P_c$), the equation indicates
a reduction in propellant flow. This results
in further lowering of the chamber pressure
during the low-pressure period. While $P_x <
P_c$, the equation indicates a greater flow.

This results in amplification of the next high-
pressure wave. If the time delay is of such a
value that it matches the frequency requirements, the amplification can rapidly result in
pressure increase of astounding ranges. Figure 15.2 illustrates this cyclic effect.

Initial excitation of this condition requires a resonance condition in the frequency
range of 10 to 100 cycles per second plus a
source of such vibration. If the resonance
condition is present, the combustion process
(or another system component) will often
initiate the servocycle.

An effective linear burning rate for the
propellant within the chamber can be expressed as

$$\bar{r} = KP^n \qquad (15\text{-}2)$$

Hence the time delay can be expressed in
terms of the pressure. It can be shown that
the burning rate exponent is a critical function in such time delays. The critical value
of the time lag is

$$t_{(\text{lag})} = K_2 \left[\pi - \cos^{-1}\left(\frac{1-n}{n} \right) \right]^{(2n-1)^{1/2}} \qquad (15\text{-}3)$$

where K_2 is a function of chamber volume,
flow coefficient, and chamber temperature.

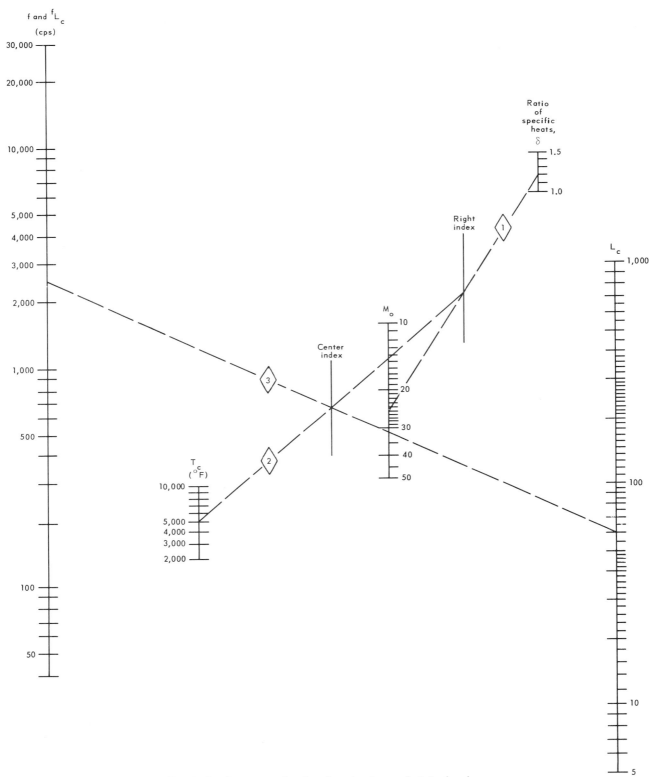

Fig. 15.3.   Resonance vibration of combustion products in chamber

However, the expression exclusive of K_2 has no values for n under 0.5. Hence, when n is less than $\frac{1}{2}$, such instability does not exist.

An approximation for the K_2 value follows

$$K_2 = gL^*/C_wRT_c \qquad (15\text{-}4)$$

However, this is an approximation based upon consideration of the system in terms of a monopropellant and a nonvarying chamber pressure. It also does not allow for specific impulse variations. However, this K_2 may be used as an approximation or determined by experiment.

High-frequency vibrations of the combustion gases range upward of 100 cycles per second. These oscillations seem to be equal to the natural frequencies of the contents of the combustion chamber. These frequencies may be longitudinal, radial, or angular. Such frequencies are functions of chamber temperature, molecular weight of the gases, ratio of specific heats of the combustion products, and the effective length of the considered dimension. The fundamental resonance vibration of the longitudinal condition can be determined from Fig. 15.3. Radial and angular modes can be approximated from Fig. 15.4. The transverse modes are more important as D_c/L_c approaches or exceeds unity. This is more common among larger engines.

The increased energy of local combustion due to the wave-front pressure increase provides amplification energy which prevents viscous dissipation decay. If the normal flame front is at a point from two- to three-fifths of the chamber length, the local burning rate will not affect resonance combustion.

Near the midpoint of chamber length, the flame-front location can be considered as providing longitudinal combustion stability in terms of the chamber resonance. When the flame front exists, as is the usual case, well forward of the midpoint of the chamber, Equation 15.3 indicates instability at certain time-lag values and burning-rate exponents. Linear and volumetric effective burning rates, local pressures, specific heat ratio deviations, local heat transfer, shock wave parameters, and vibration frequencies are all interactive as related to time lag, pressure fronts, and chamber configurations.

The transverse sloshing mode is of greater importance as the over-all volume is increased without the length's being extended to any great degree. In engines with very high thrusts, sloshing vibration must be considered. Figure 15.4 gives such frequencies from a knowledge of the fundamental longitudinal mode; f_{L_c} is determined from Figure 15.3.

Surging in the feed system, as a result of oscillations in the storage tanks or pressurizing system (hence surging of propellant from the injector), can propagate frequencies in the low, intermediate, or high range. In the low or high range, chamber resonance or servo-resonance results. In the intermediate range, component resonance may serve to amplify the condition.

A special intermediate range frequency is

$$f = 2f_c(1 + f_c t_s)^{-1} \qquad (15\text{-}5)$$

where

f_c = natural frequency of combustion products for the chamber

t_s = chamber stay time.

This frequency results from the disturbance of the propellant mixture ratio by resonance or shock wave. The mixing and evaporation process does not proceed as usual. A percentage of the fuel or oxidizer remains isolated throughout the chamber and enters the nozzle in a partially reacted state. This wave of oxidizer or fuel undergoes chemical reaction throughout the chamber and on into

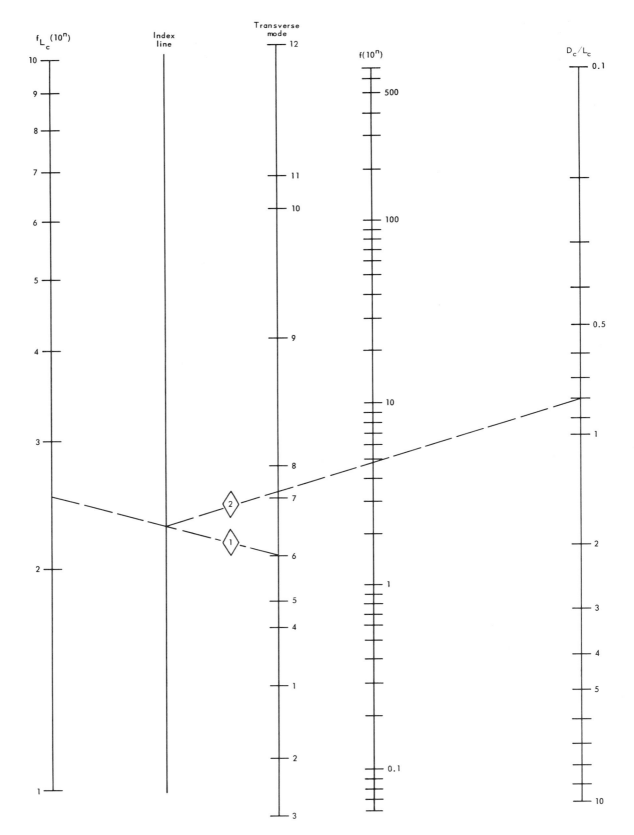

Fig. 15.4. Primary transverse vibration in combustion chambers

the nozzle. A shock wave results as this entropy wave enters the nozzle. The shock wave sweeps upstream to the injector where the fuel ratio is again disturbed. This results in a new imbalance which again flows downstream to the nozzle. A new shock wave results. This cycle continues at the frequency expressed by Equation 15.5.

In order to study the gas resonance correctly, the natural frequencies of the components must be known. Surging in the oxidizer and fuel tanks must also be studied.

Injector plate vibration

Vibration of the injector plate is of major consideration. It can serve to transmit vibrations from the feed system into the chamber. Moreover, it is exposed to vibration characteristics of the chamber and its contents. Its resonance can stimulate adverse oscillations within the chamber.

If the injector plate is designed as a rectangular plate, Fig. 15-5 should be used to determine the fundamental frequency. If it is a circular plate, Fig. 15.6 should be used. If the material is other than steel, Fig. 15.7 may be used to convert the natural frequency of the configuration in steel to the frequency in the selected material.

If the plate is held in place by a ring, the ring vibration should be determined by Fig. 15.8.

Nozzle vibration

Nozzle vibration often leads to resonant excitation of other components of the engine. If its natural frequency is reasonably close to that of the combustion products, malfunction often results. As the nozzle is subject to a wide range of exciting frequencies, it may easily become excited. If its natural frequency is within an undesired range, it may serve as a transducer and amplifier.

The nozzle natural frequency may be determined from Figs. 15.9 and 15.10. For materials other than steel, Fig. 15.7 may be used to convert the frequencies obtained from the foregoing charts to the natural frequency of the material under construction.

The nozzle, like the injector, is in a critical region and the resonance should be compared with the resonance values of other components in the system.

Chamber vibration

Resonance of the chamber itself can lead most directly to longitudinal or radial vibration of the combustion products. Resonant vibrations can excite the injector plate or the gas volume directly. Such frequencies can exist as ring frequencies or in longitudinal modes.

Chamber cross-sectional frequencies can be determined from Fig. 15.8. Fundamental frequencies of the chamber can be deduced from Figs. 15.11 and 15.12.

Storage tank resonance

Vibrations in the metal configuration of the storage tank can be determined like those in the combustion chamber from Figs. 15.8, 15.11, and 15.12.

Resonance of the tank contents can be determined from Fig. 15.13. Slosh frequencies can be determined from Figs. 15.14 and 15.15 for spherical and cylindrical tanks, respectively. This is a function of the propellant temperature and properties of both the liquid and the configuration.

If resonance of the tank contents is in the correct range, the turbopump can serve to increase the wave amplitude. Surging of the propellant in feed lines and injector can result. In addition, this vibration, like all other sources, can cause physical shaking and possible destruction of the rocket, both frame and engine.

Structural members and tubing

Vibration of structural members is treated in Fig. 15.16. Supports and beam-like structures can be studied directly by means of this graph. Resonance for materials other than steel can be determined by frequency conversion from Fig. 15.7.

Nuts, bolts, rods, tubes, circular and rectangular plates, rings (cross sections such as the rocket case), etc., may be studied by use of the related nomograph.

Tubing in straight segments can be studied as beams using Fig. 15.16. Other segments must be studied in terms of the over-all tubing configuration; for example, coils must be considered in terms of spring vibration.

Tubing is important as a transmission medium between storage tanks and the turbo-pump system and between the turbo-pump system and combustion chamber. If its resonance frequencies are within the range of frequencies being transmitted, excitation is more likely. It is important for the designer to remember that the vibration of a seemingly isolated component may be the source of malfunction via resonance.

Chugging or screaming (high-frequency resonance) may be eliminated by changing chamber configuration, injector design, or propellant properties. Such conditions may also be corrected by eliminating the excitor source.

High-frequency resonance may result in excessive local heat transfer. This can cause 'hot spots' and burnout of the chamber and/or nozzle wall. To prevent this, the chamber length must be changed or the propellant properties altered.

Seldom would all modes of vibration be operative. However, few designs can avoid at least one mode of resonance. Design in terms of vibration is usually a compromise when all factors are known.

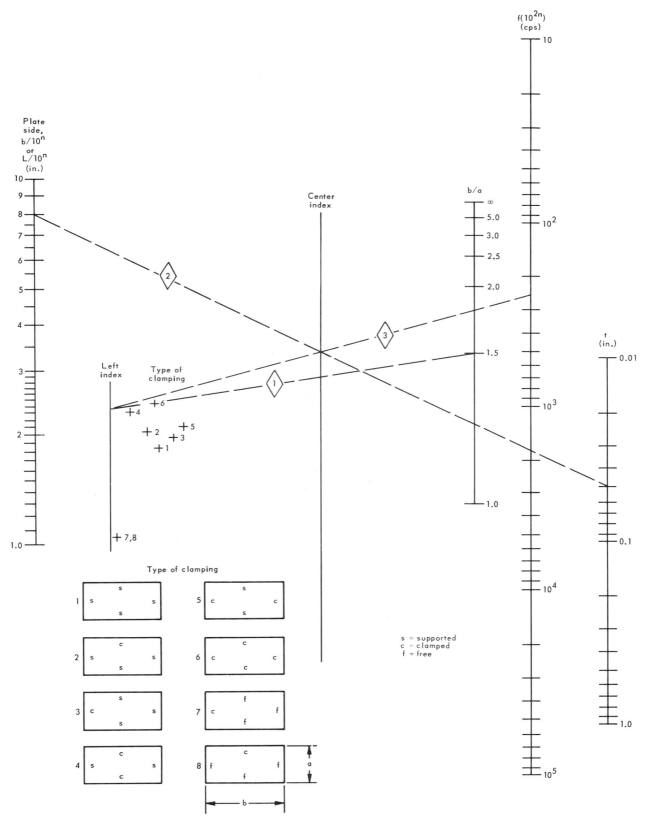

Fig. 15.5. Vibration of rectangular steel plates (fundamental natural frequency)

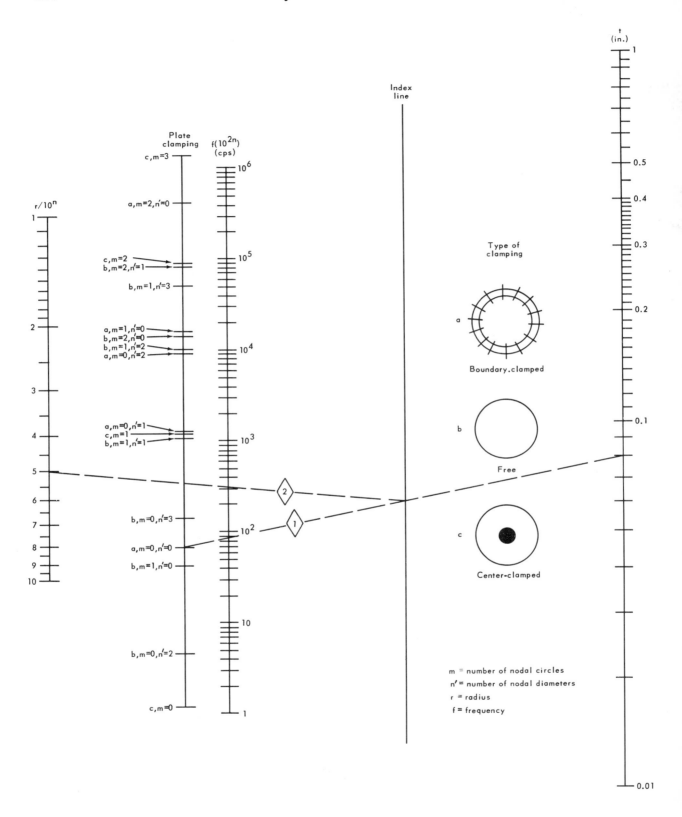

Fig. 15.6. Vibration of circular steel plates

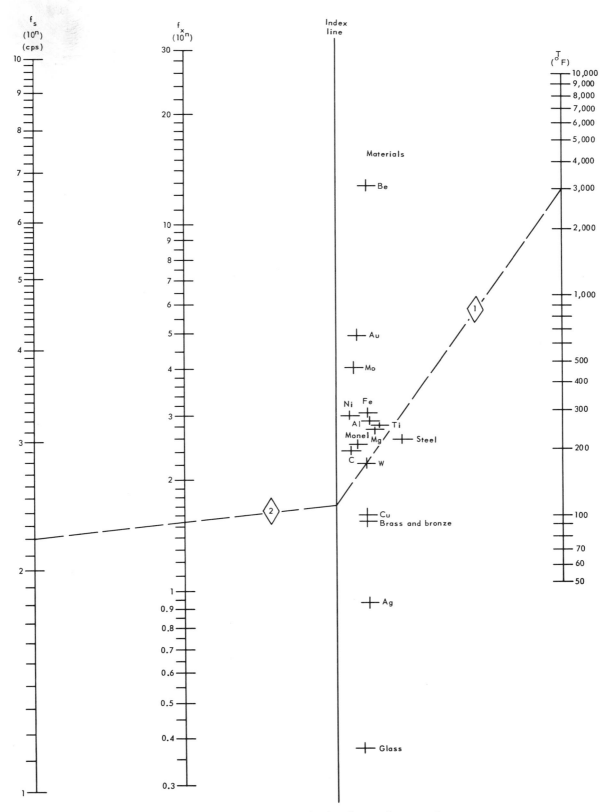

Fig. 15.7. Frequency conversion for materials other than steel at operating temperatures

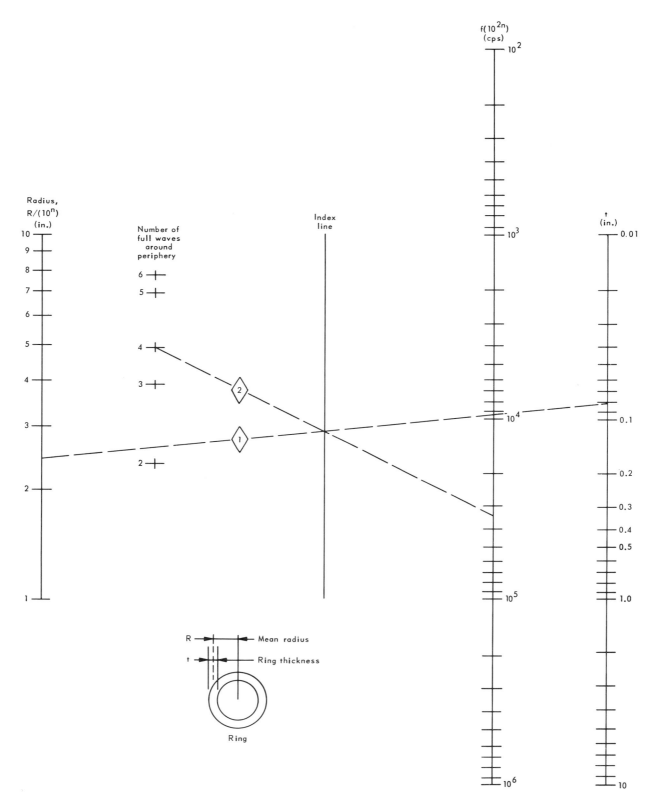

Fig. 15.8. Vibration in circular steel ring (or cross section of cylinder)

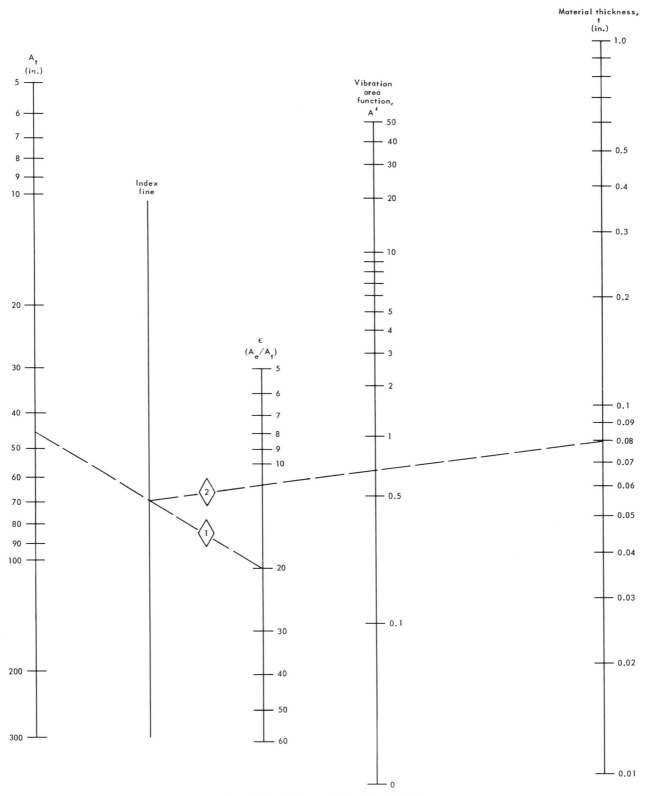

Fig. 15.9. Steel nozzle vibration (No. 1)

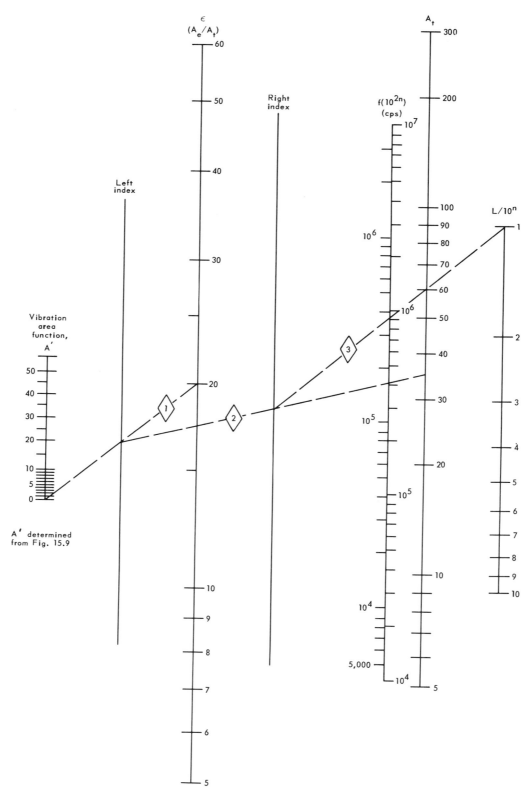

Fig. 15.10.   Steel nozzle vibration (No. 2)

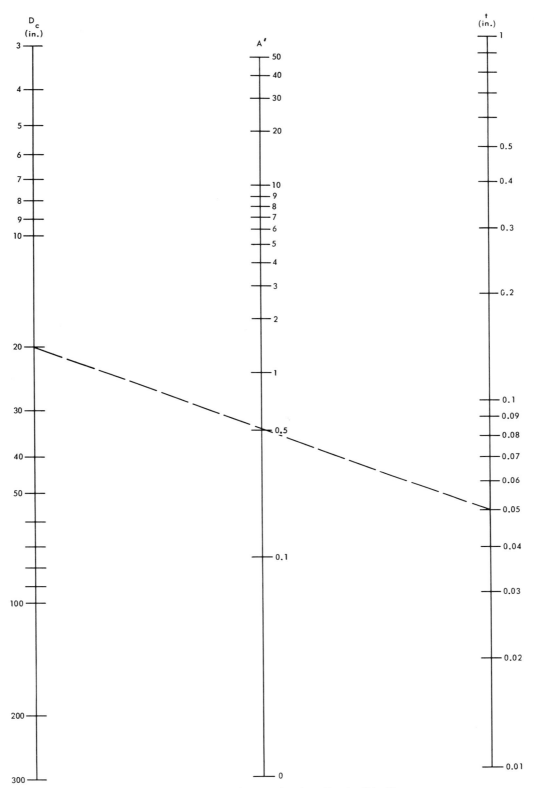

Fig. 15.11. Steel combustion chamber vibration (No. 1)

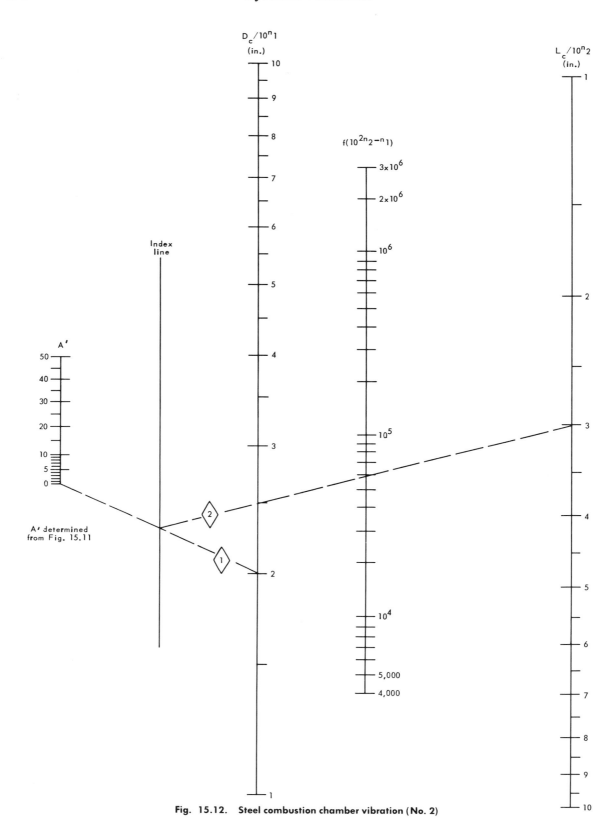

Fig. 15.12. Steel combustion chamber vibration (No. 2)

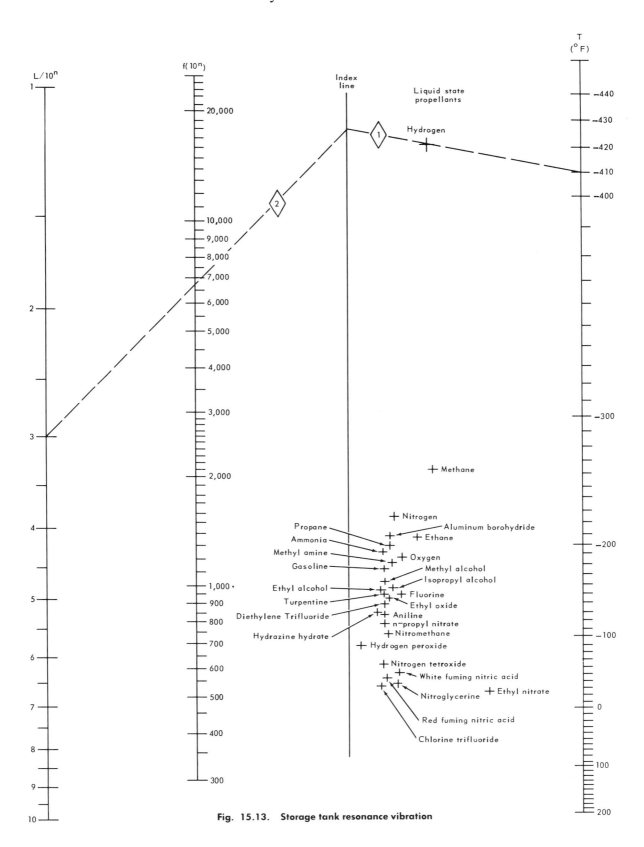

Fig. 15.13.   Storage tank resonance vibration

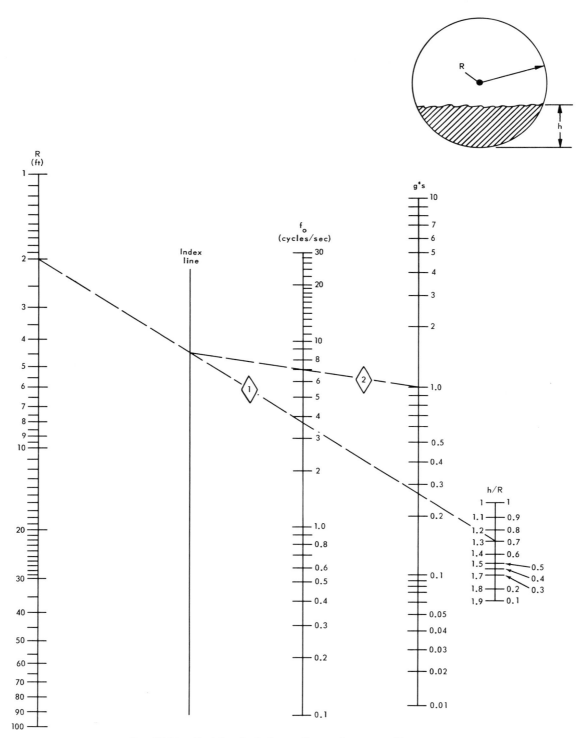

Fig. 15.14. Slosh in spherical propellant tanks—natural frequency

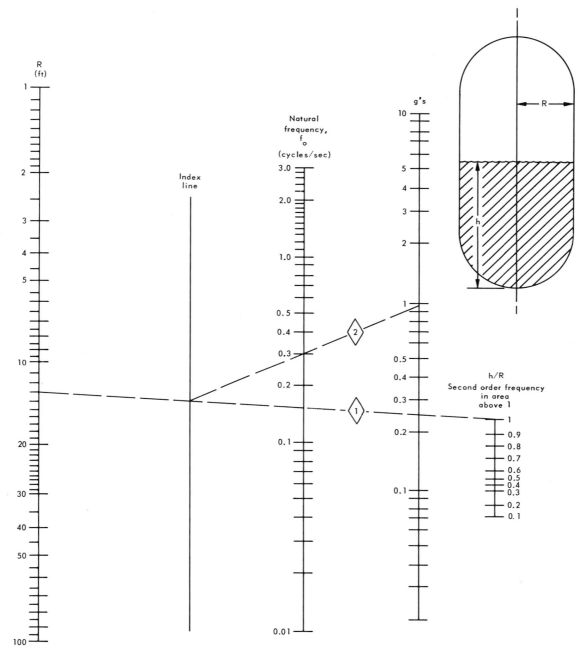

Fig. 15.15. Slosh in cylindrical propellant tanks—natural frequency

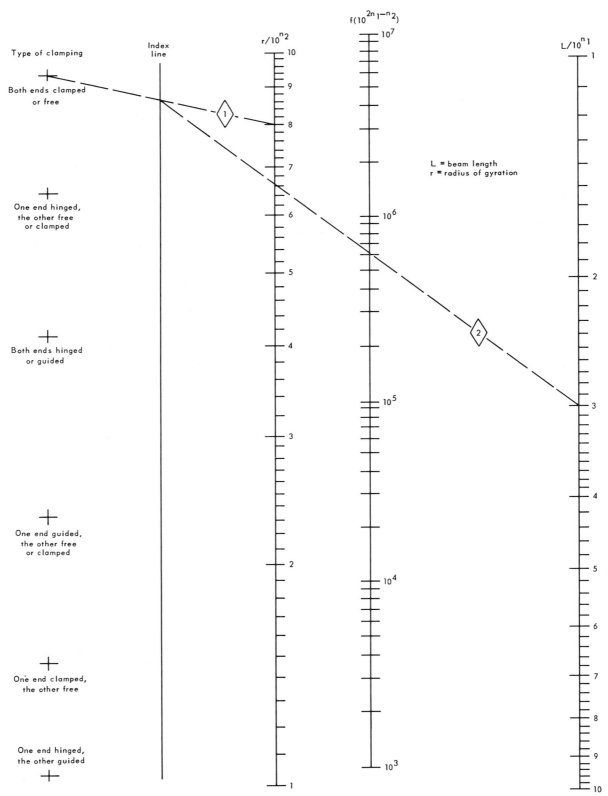

Fig. 15.16. Vibration in steel beams

Section IV

HYBRID DESIGN

16

Hybrid Systems

Hybrid systems incorporate many of the advantages and disadvantages of the separate systems. The bringing together of the complexities of liquid engines with the compactness and simplification of a solid system improves the reliability but poses new problems. The improved reliability parameters are illustrated in Fig. 16.1, which compares liquid and hybrid reliability for similar configurations. Hybrid engines may prove optimal where needs for high reliability and off-on or variable control exist simultaneously.

There is a discrepancy between the upper ranges of specific impulse for solid liquid designs. Liquid engines can achieve much greater specific impulse, for example, by the use of fluorine hydrogen combinations while solids are limited by chemical properties of the solid propellants. However, solids are apt to have a greater density impulse. Figure 16.2 relates these general ranges of specific impulse for solid, liquid, and hybrid design. It is possible that hybrid design can optimize specific impulse and density parameters.

The over-all mating of the liquid and solid systems is illustrated in Fig. 16.3. The upper part of the diagram illustrates the liquid section of the system. The oxidizer is supplied from a storage tank via a turbo-pump to the combustion chamber, which, in the solid unit, consists of an injector, a solid fuel grain, and a nozzle.

This mating reduces the number of components needed to about half that of a liquid system. The nozzle can be liquid-cooled, if desired, but the chamber is insulated by the grain. A more advanced system utilizing a turbine gas tap is diagrammed in Fig. 16.4. Compactness, high density, and reliability are inherent in the solid half of the design, whereas controllability and optimization of specific impulse are attributable to the liquid half of the design.

A solid catalyst is often employed to cause monopropellant release of energy as illustrated in Figs. 16.5 and 16.6, but these are not true hybrid systems and should be studied in terms of a single propellant liquid engine.

195

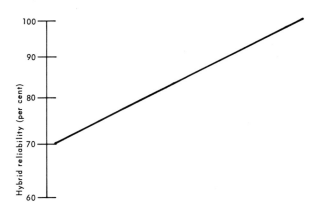

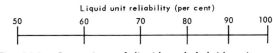

Fig. 16.1. Comparison of liquid and hybrid unit reliability

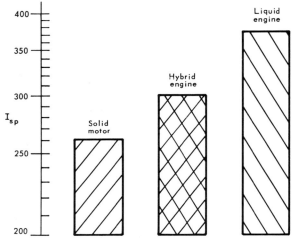

Fig. 16.2. Typical ranges of specific impulse

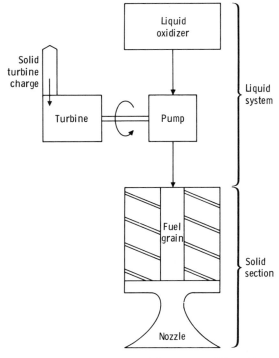

Fig. 16.3. Hybrid liquid-solid system (solid turbine charge)

Weight flow

Hybrid weight flow represents the sum of the liquid weight flow and the solid weight flow:

$$\dot{W} = \dot{W}_o + \dot{W}_f = \dot{W}_{(liquid)} + \dot{W}_{(solid)} \quad (16\text{-}1)$$

This relationship can be expressed in terms of liquid oxidizer and solid fuel (the terms can be interchanged if the states are reversed in design):

$$\dot{W} = \dot{W}_o + A_c cd P_c^n \quad (16\text{-}2)$$

where c = burning coefficient.

This expression relates the desired oxidizer flow, the pressure, and the grain burning area. A direct relationship between the pressure and burning area via the fuel ratio is given by the following formula:

$$\dot{W} = (1 + \dot{r})(cd)A_c P_c^n \quad (16\text{-}3)$$

This relationship is expressed in Fig. 16.7.

This in turn can be directly related to the flow coefficient by the standard formulation,

$$\dot{W} = C_w A_t P_c \quad (16\text{-}4)$$

Burning area

The required burning area must meet the requirements of the following solid propellant flow formula:

$$A_c = (\dot{W} - \dot{W}_o)(C_w A_t)^n / cd_f \dot{W}^n \quad (16\text{-}5)$$

This can be expressed as

$$A_c = \dot{W}_o / r\dot{r}d_f \quad (16\text{-}6)$$

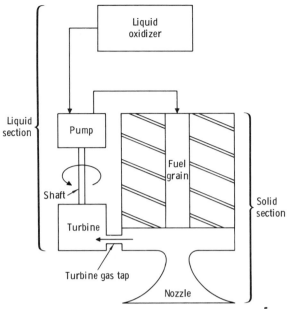

Fig. 16.4. Hybrid liquid-solid system (turbine gas tap)

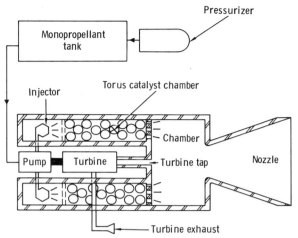

Fig. 16.6. Monopropellant-catalyst engine (large-scale)

thus relating oxidizer flow to burning rate and density. Expressed in terms of thrust-to-specific-impulse ratio, the following formula

is useful in initial design:

$$A_c = (F/I_{sp})^{(1-n)}(C_w A_t)^n/(1 + \dot{r})cd \qquad (16\text{-}7)$$

Perforational configurations can be developed via the equations presented in the section on solid grain design.

Stay time

The stay time of a hybrid rocket combustion chamber is indicative of the time that would be required for a molecule of reacting gas to travel from injector to nozzle. The mean stay time is the average time for such a molecule to travel through the grain. The stay time is a maximum stay time if free port areas are considered. The mean stay time is often a more reliable parameter in terms of grain performance.

The stay time can be estimated by the following relationship

$$t_s = V_c M_o/12 \, R C_w A_t T_c \qquad (16\text{-}8)$$

Increasing the grain cross-sectional area or the free port area, hence increasing V_c, increases the stay time. Using a larger throat area decreases the stay time. Stay time is inversely related to the temperature.

The mean stay time can be computed via the formula

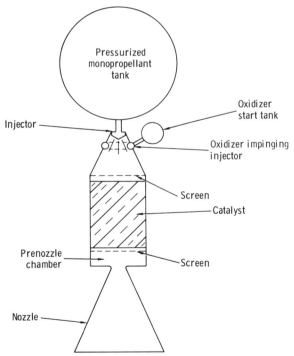

Fig. 16.5. Monopropellant-catalyst engine (small-scale)

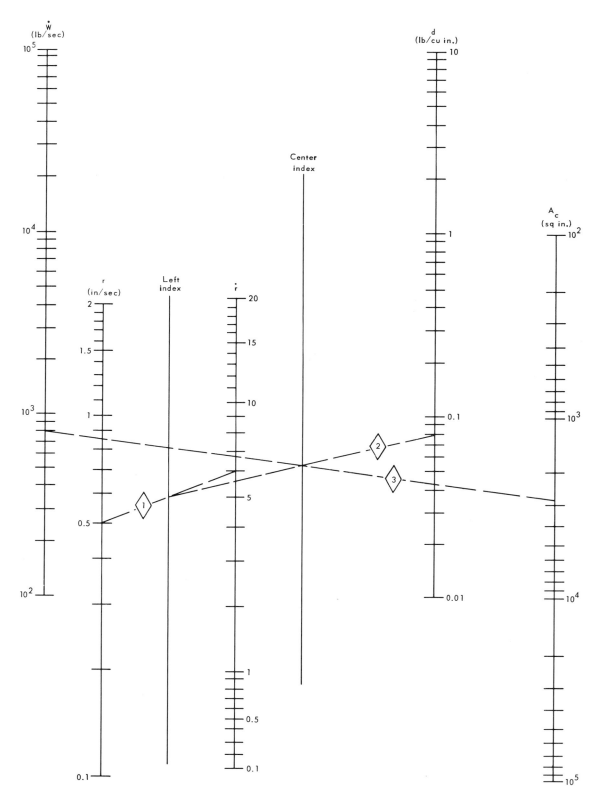

Fig. 16.7. Hybrid weight flow

$$t_{(mean)} = P_c A_p L M_o / 24 R A_c r T_c d(1 + \dot{r}) \quad (16\text{-}9)$$

A mean stay time inclusive of free port area to optimize hybrid design—that is, reduce free port area to a minimum—can be computed from

$$t_{s(mean)} = V_c M_o P_c^{(1-n)} / 24 R A_c T_c (1 + \dot{r}) c d_f \quad (16\text{-}10)$$

where

V_c = free port volume plus grain duct volume

M_o = molecular weight of combustion products

P_c = chamber pressure

R = gas constant

T_c = chamber temperature

A_c = grain burning area

d = grain density

A_p = cross-sectional area of the grain.

Investigation of these formulations indicates that the most critical stay time occurs at ignition. As the cross-sectional grain port area increases during combustion, the stay time increases in direct relationship.

The fuel ratio

The fuel ratio is

$$\dot{r} = \dot{W}_o / \dot{W}_f \quad (16\text{-}11)$$

In hybrid design this can be related in the following way

$$\dot{r} = \dot{W}_o / r d A_c \quad (16\text{-}12)$$

or from total weight flow and burning area

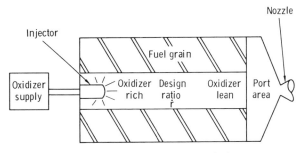

Fig. 16.8. Illustration of effective fuel ratio

$$\dot{r} = (\dot{W} / A_c r d) - 1 \quad (16\text{-}13)$$

In terms of thrust and specific impulse, the following provides a close approximation for the required fuel ratio

$$\dot{r} = (F - I_{sp} c A_c P_c^n d) / I_{sp} c A_c P_c^n d \quad (16\text{-}14)$$

This design ratio will approximate the value at the mid-reaction point in the grain as illustrated in Fig. 16.8. Correct design ratio will maximize specific impulse or density impulse. Erosive and effective functions are indicated by Fig. 16.9 (as applied to Fig. 16.8), which illustrates the tendency of the effective fuel ratio to decrease along the grain length simultaneously with the erosive burning effect, adding additional fuel.

Characteristic chamber length

The characteristic chamber length is the ratio of the chamber volume to the nozzle throat area. This is the parameter that indicates the propellant stay time characteristics. Certain propellant combinations exhibit certain characteristic chamber length requirements. Hybrid characteristic chamber lengths, L^*, do not precisely indicate stay time values. Mean values are perhaps more useful because, without a pre-nozzle area to complete combustion, combustion products enter the nozzle in a state of incomplete reaction.

The characteristic length can be expressed as

$$L^* = L_c (A_p / A_t) \quad (16\text{-}15)$$

where L_c = grain length.

To this basic length, if a prenozzle port area is utilized, the characteristic length of the free port area must be added:

$$L^* = L_c (A_p / A_t) + V_{port} / A_t \quad (16\text{-}16)$$

where

A_p = cross-sectional area of the grain

A_t = throat area

$V_{(port)}$ = free port volume.

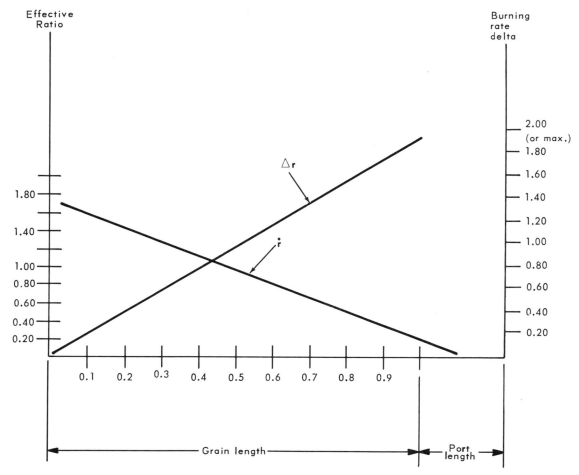

Fig. 16.9. Effective fuel ratio and erosive burning rate

Use of a free port prevents shock due to incomplete reactants entering the throat area, but experiments have shown that small but continuous input of incomplete products produce stable conditions.

Burning rates

Burning rates of hybrid grains are complex functions depending upon many parameters. The effects of erosive burning increase the comparative burning rate toward the nozzle end of the grain. In addition, the pressure tends to increase the rate toward the forward end. The rate is also subject to the density of oxidizer present, as illustrated in Fig. 16.9.

The basic burning rate equation,

$$r = c(P_c)^n \qquad (16\text{-}17)$$

can be altered to include the increase due to erosive burning, as follows:

$$r = cP_c^n\left\{1 + \left[\frac{2K_e\dot{W}_i(2/\gamma - 1)^{1/(\gamma-1)}}{P_o A_p C_w}\right]\right\}$$

$$(16\text{-}18)$$

where

K_e = erosive constant

$\dot{W}_i$ = weight flow at station under study

P_o = fore end pressure

P_c = station chamber pressure.

Relating the burning rate to the weight flow leads to

$$r = (\dot{W} - \dot{W}_o)/A_c d \qquad (16\text{-}19)$$

Another expression that relates the total weight flow, the flow ratio, and the burning area is

$$r = \dot{W}/(1 + \dot{r})A_c d \qquad (16\text{-}20)$$

A useful relationship that includes the throat area to burning surface ratio is

$$r = (A_t/A_c)[C_w/(1 + \dot{r})d] \qquad (16\text{-}21)$$

Hybrid design may be accomplished by using the appropriate liquid and solid design nomographs for each section of the total system.

The needed web and the distance burned may be determined from Fig. 6.1.

The burning rate may be determined from Figs. 8.3 and 8.4.

The turbo-pump system can be designed by means of the graphs in the section on liquid turbo-pump design, with consideration given to one pump instead of two. The injector and other components may also be designed by means of graphs already presented.

Grain geometry and other grain design may be developed by means of the graphs and equations in the solid design section of the text.

The weight flow relationship between solid and liquid phases can be determined by means of Fig. 11.4. The weight flow-burning area relationships may be determined from Fig. 16.7.

The graphs in Chapter 2 on general relationships, such as pressure and specific impulse, may be used to establish these parameters.

Section V

STRUCTURES

17

Structures: Storage Tanks, Chambers, and Airframe

The airframe of a rocket is an integral part of the system and cannot be treated separately from the engine. The inert weight of the structures must be known to define fully any mission that was indicated in Chapter 1. Solid rocket cases are generally utilized as the airframe. Liquid rocket propellant tanks may be likewise utilized. In order to define the total system, a study should include the interaction of such components.

Figure 17.1 illustrates some typical over-all rocket configurations. A two-stage rocket is illustrated at upper left. The upper stage is designed in the same manner as a single-stage rocket. The booster is designed to include the upper stage as its payload. As rocket size increases, the design becomes more complex. The large scale rocket at upper right has a booster that in essence is a scaled-up small rocket, but the large unit at lower left is a clustered design booster, and the unit to the right of that is a segmented design.

When large numbers of segments or clustered units are used, there are not only weight penalties, but reliability may be lowered as indicated by Fig. 17.2.

Airframe stress in cylinders may be studied by means of Figs. 17.3, 17.4, and 17.5. The use of these nomographs is discussed under case design below. Bending stress may be determined from Fig. 17.6. Volume and surface areas may be estimated by means of Figs. 17.7 and 17.8. Weight can be estimated from Fig. 17.9.

Cylindrical tanks

Cylindrical propellant tanks (see Diagram A, Fig. 17.10.) are the most common types of tanks in use. They maintain the same over-all configuration as the total vehicle.

Stress may be determined from Figs. 17.3, 17.4, 17.5. Bending stress may be estimated from Fig. 17.6.

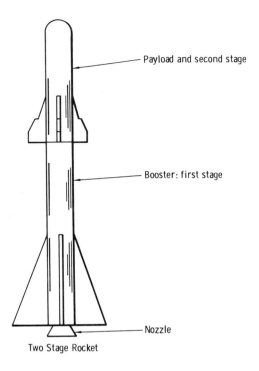

Payload and second stage

Booster: first stage

Nozzle

Two Stage Rocket

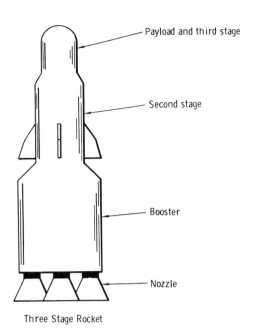

Payload and third stage

Second stage

Booster

Nozzle

Three Stage Rocket

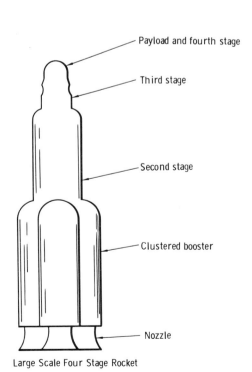

Payload and fourth stage

Third stage

Second stage

Clustered booster

Nozzle

Large Scale Four Stage Rocket

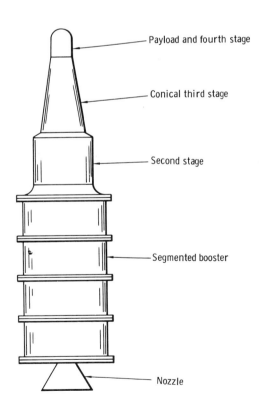

Payload and fourth stage

Conical third stage

Second stage

Segmented booster

Nozzle

Fig. 17.1. Typical rocket configurations

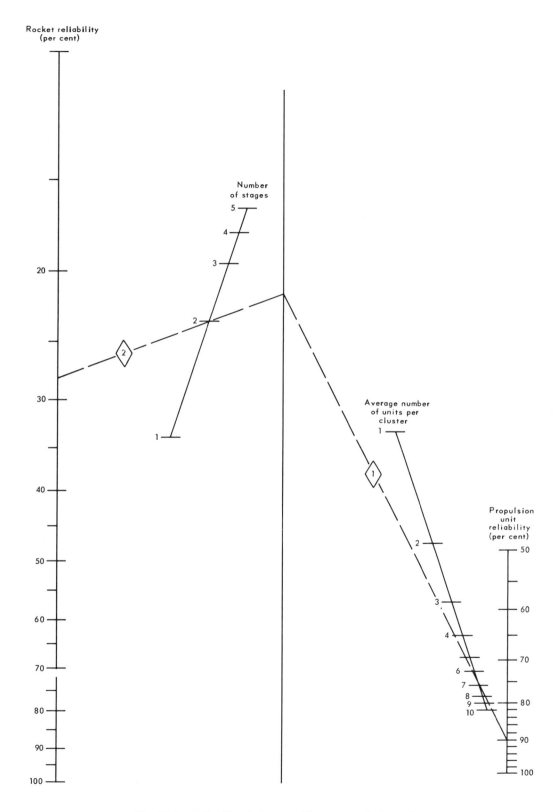

Fig. 17.2. Reliability of cluster and/or segment design rockets

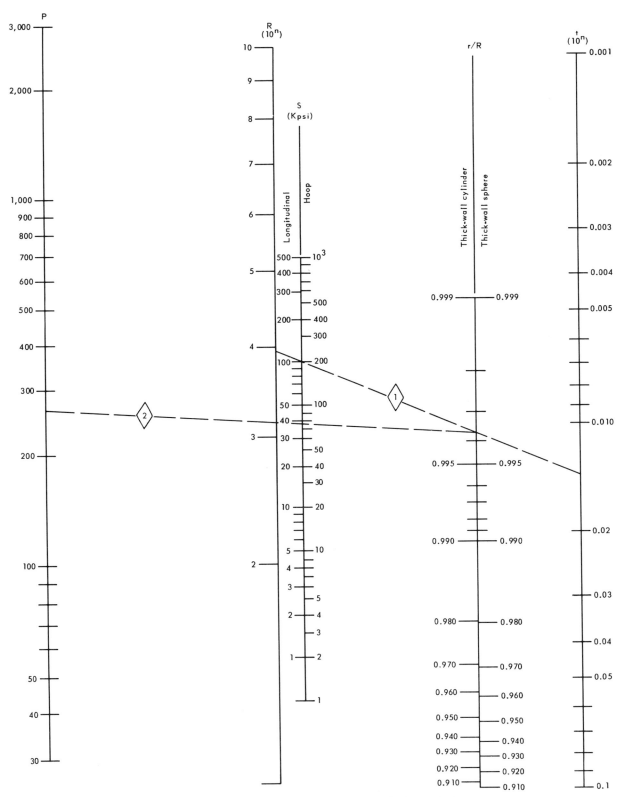

Fig. 17.3. Stress in chambers, tanks, and other cylinders and spheres

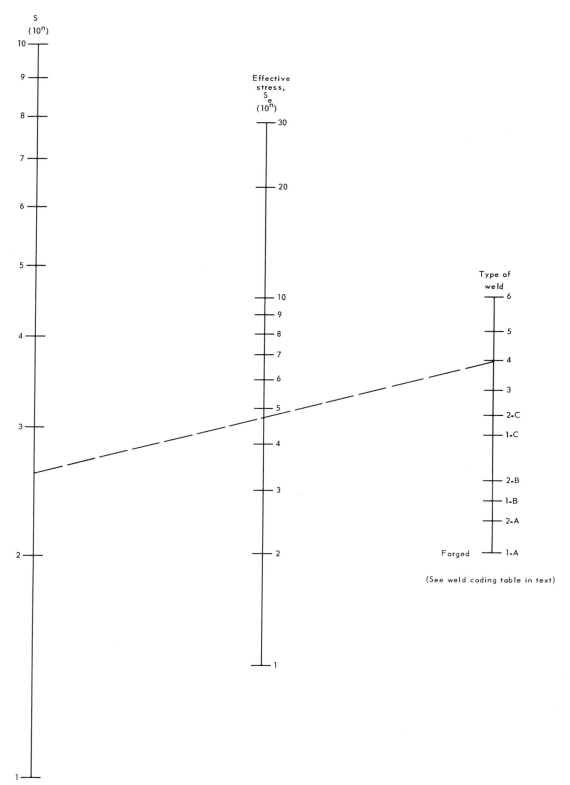

Fig. 17.4. Longitudinal weld stress in cylinders

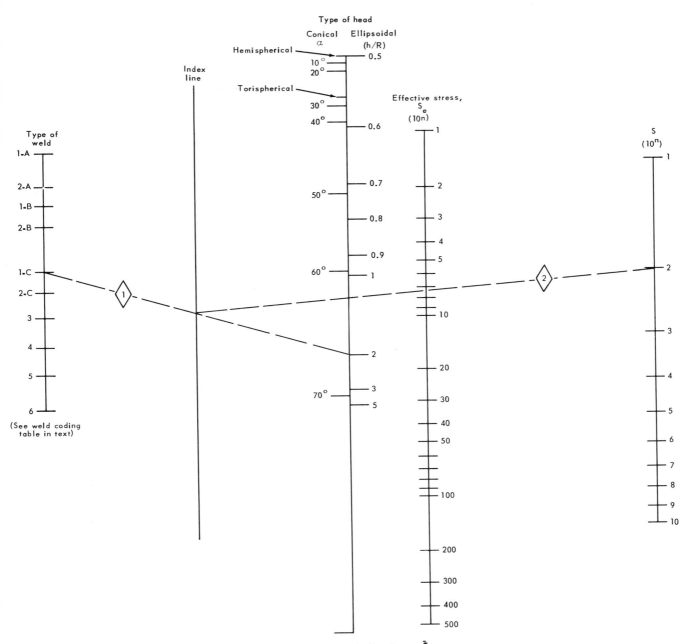

Fig. 17.5. Cylinder head stress

For conical heads, α = included 1/2 angle; for ellipsoidal heads, h/R = ratio of head depth to cylinder radius.

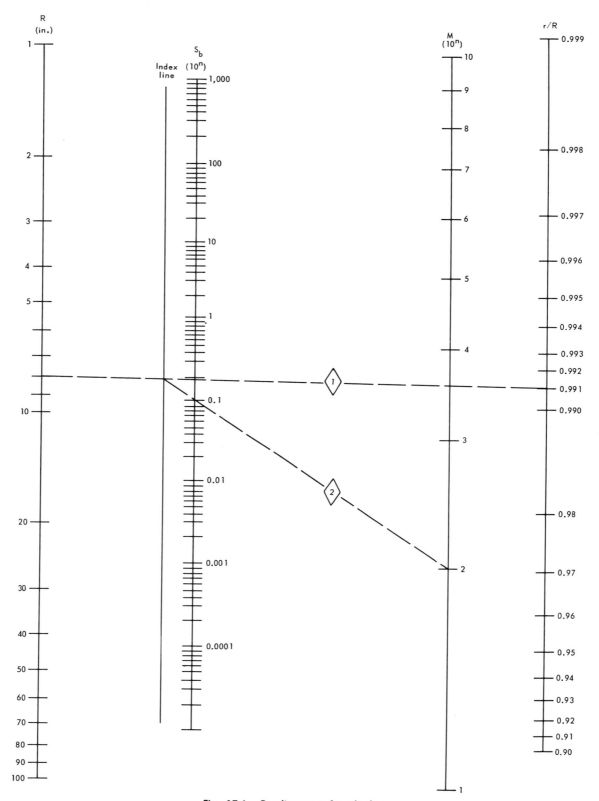

Fig. 17.6. Bending stress for cylinders

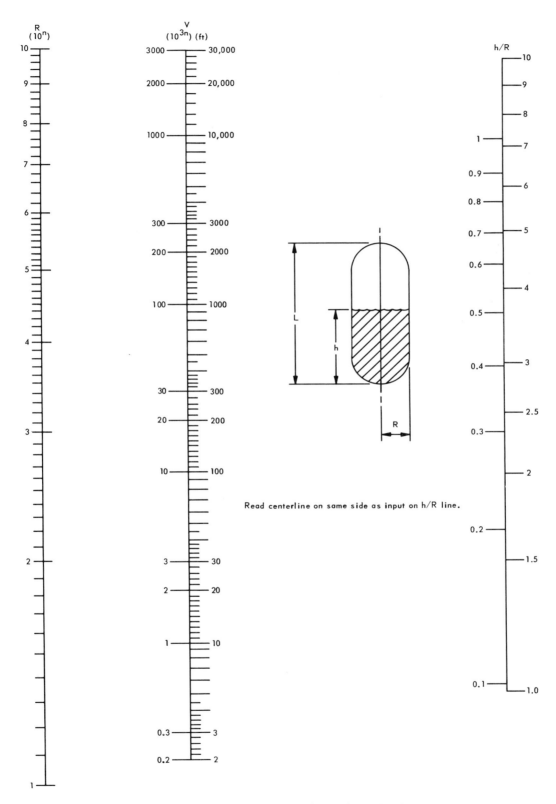

Read centerline on same side as input on h/R line.

Fig. 17.7.   Volume of propellant tank cylinder or sphere when $h < L - r$

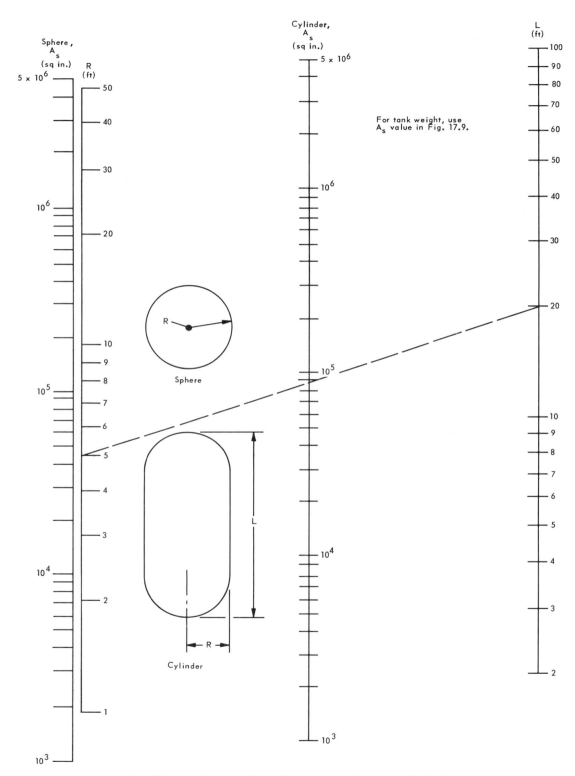

Fig. 17.8. Surface area of propellant tanks—spherical or cylindrical

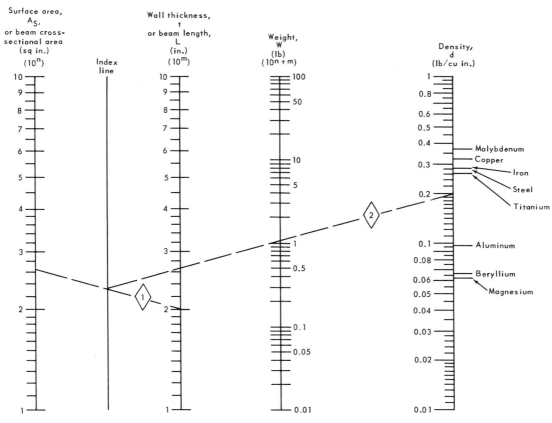

Surface area,
A_S,
or beam cross-
sectional area
(sq in.)
(10^n)

Index
line

Wall thickness,
t
or beam length,
L
(in.)
(10^m)

Weight,
W
(lb)
(10^{n+m})

Density,
d
(lb/cu in.)

Fig. 17.9. Weight

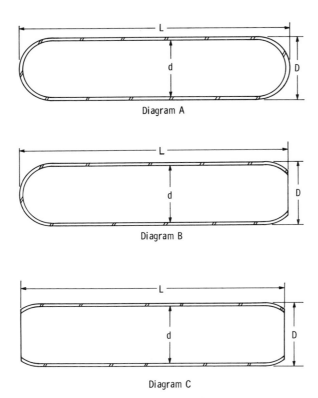

Diagram A

Diagram B

Diagram C

Fig. 17.10. Basic case configuration

Volume and surface area studies may be estimated by Figs. 17.7 and 17.8.

Weight may be determined from Fig. 17.9 by entering A_s and t.

Spherical tanks

Spheres provide optimal volume-to-weight relationships. They are often used in final stage designs. This type of tank is illustrated in Fig. 16.5.

Stress may be estimated from Figs. 17.3, 17.4, and 17.5.

Volume and surface area studies may be made by means of Figs. 17.8 and 17.11.

Weight may be determined by means of Fig. 17.9 by entering A_s and t.

Torus tanks

Torus tanks provide utilization of space not available to other configurations.

Stress may be estimated from Fig. 17.12.

Volume and surface area studies may be made via Figs. 17.13 and 17.14.

Weight may be determined via Fig. 17.9 by entering A_s and t.

Tubing

Tubing may be studied as round hollow beams by means of Figs. 17.15, 17.16, 17.17, 17.18, and 17.19. It may also be studied by means of the cylinder charts.

Stress may be determined from Figs. 17.3, 17.4, and 17.5.

Weight may be determined from Fig. 9.13 or from Fig. 17.9 by entering cross-sectional areas and length.

Structural components and beams

Plates, flanges, and other structural components can be treated as beams. Weight studies of wires and tubing can also be studied as beams.

The bending moment is determined from Table 17.1 and Fig. 17.15. The section modulus is determined from Table 17.2 and Fig. 17.17. The bending stress is then determined from Fig. 17.18.

The cross-sectional area is determined from Table 17.2 and Fig. 17.16. With this cross-sectional area and the beam length, the weight is determined from Fig. 17.9.

Flange weight

Flanges may represent a weight penalty in rocket design. Segmented designs often utilize flanges as illustrated in Figs. 7.34 and 7.35. Some solid rockets may use a welded fore end but have a flanged aft end assembly that includes the nozzle as illustrated in Fig. 6.9. Flange weight may be

Table 17.1.   Beam bending moments

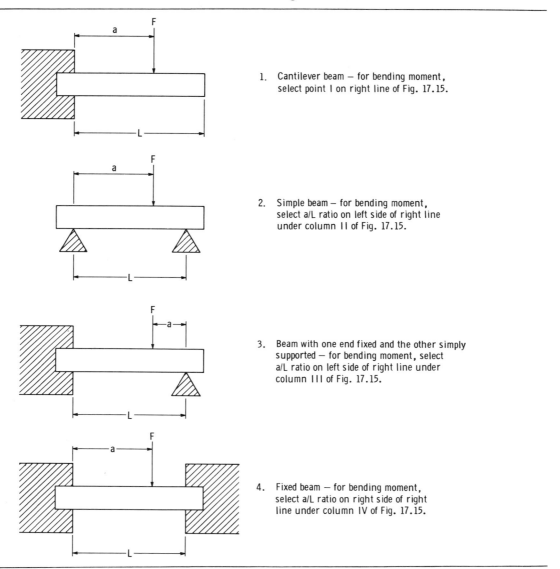

1. Cantilever beam — for bending moment, select point I on right line of Fig. 17.15.

2. Simple beam — for bending moment, select a/L ratio on left side of right line under column II of Fig. 17.15.

3. Beam with one end fixed and the other simply supported — for bending moment, select a/L ratio on left side of right line under column III of Fig. 17.15.

4. Fixed beam — for bending moment, select a/L ratio on right side of right line under column IV of Fig. 17.15.

determined by using Table 17.2. Figure 17.16 determines the cross section area. The D and d values illustrated in Fig. 17.19 are entered as B or H and b or h respectively in Fig. 17.16 to get the area value. With this area value, $X_1 + X_2$ (see Fig. 17.19) is entered as L in Fig. 17.9 to determine the weight. When a conical condition exists such as that illustrated in Diagram B of Fig. 17.19, the mean value of d is entered as h or b in Fig. 17.16.

Combustion chamber and nozzles

Combustion chambers and both liquid and solid rocket nozzles are exposed to high temperature gases and internal pressures. The stresses must be considered at elevated temperature ranges. The chambers may be considered as cylindrical with the basic configuration illustrated in Fig. 17.10. The nozzles are treated as cones with hoop stress.

Table 17.2.   Beam section modulus and area

Enter B'/B on left line in Fig. 17.17. Then enter B/H to determine f(I/c), which is the section modulus.

For area, enter the ratio of B'/B in Fig. 17.16. The B'/B function applies to any of the 'rectangle' symbol beams.

Enter B'/B as zero in Fig. 17.17 to determine f(I/c), which is the section modulus.

For area, select the triangle symbol in Fig. 17.16.

Enter B'/B as zero in Fig. 17.17. Enter B/H to determine $f(I/c)_1$. Enter b/H to determine $f(I/c)_2$. Subtract $f(I/c)_2$ from $f(I/c)_1$ to determine the section modulus.

For area, first enter H, B values in Fig. 17.16, then enter h, b values. Subtract the second output from the first for the area.

Enter 1.0 on the B'/B line in Fig. 17.17. Then determine $f(I/c)_1$ by entering B/H. Then enter b/H to determine $f(I/c)_2$. Subtract $f(I/c)_2$ from $f(I/c)_1$ to determine the section modulus.

For area, select rectangle symbol in Fig. 17.16 and then enter B, H value, then h, b value. Subtract second output from first for area.

Enter 1.0 on the B'/B line in Fig. 17.17. Then enter B/H to determine $f(I/c)_1$. Then enter b/H to determine $f(I/c)_2$, which is subtracted from $f(I/c)_1$ to determine the section modulus.

For area, select rectangle symbol in Fig. 17.16. Then enter H, B value, then h, b value. Subtract second output from first for area.

Enter 1.0 on the B'/B line in Fig. 17.17. Enter B/H to determine $f(I/c)_1$, then b/H to determine $f(I/c)_2$. Add these to determine the section modulus.

For area, select rectangle symbol in Fig. 17.16. Then enter H, B value, then h, b value. Add these outputs for area.

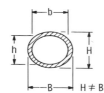

Select the circle symbol on the B'/B line in Fig. 17.17. Enter B/H to determine $f(I/c)_1$. Enter b/H to determine $f(I/c)_2$. Subtract $f(I/c)_2$ from $f(I/c)_1$ to determine the section modulus.

For area, select circle symbol in Fig. 17.16. Then enter H, B values. Then enter h, b values. Subtract second output from first to determine area.

Table 17.2.   Beam section modulus and area (cont.)

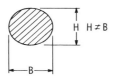

Select the circle symbol in Fig. 17.17 and enter B/H to determine the section modulus, which is f(I/c).

For area, select circle symbol in Fig. 17.16 and enter H, B values.

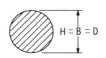

Select the circle symbol in Fig. 17.17 and enter B/H as 1.0 to determine f(I/c), which is the section modulus.

For area, select circle symbol in Fig. 17.16 and enter H, B values (in this case, H=B).

Select the circle symbol in Fig. 17.17 and enter B/H as unity to determine $f(I/c)_1$. Enter b/H to determine $f(I/c)_2$. Subtract $f(I/c)_2$ from $f(I/c)_1$ to determine the section modulus.

For area, select circle symbol in Fig. 17.16. Enter B, H values, then h, b values. Subtract second output from first to determine area.

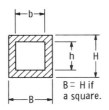

Enter B'/B as 1.0 (or exact value) in Fig. 17.17. Then enter B/H to determine $f(I/c)_1$. Then enter b/H to determine $f(I/c)_2$, which is subtracted from $f(I/c)_1$ to determine the section modulus.

For area, select rectangle symbol in Fig. 17.16. Then enter H, B values, then h, b, values. Subtract second output from first to determine area.

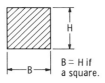

Enter B/H in Fig. 17.17 to determine the section modulus which is read as f(I/c).

For area, select rectangle symbol in Fig. 17.16. Then enter H, B values for area output.

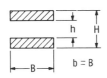

Enter B/H in Fig. 17.17 to determine both $f(I/c)_1$ and $f(I/c)_2$. The second function is subtracted from the first to obtain the section modulus.

For area, select rectangle symbol in Fig. 17.16. Then enter H, B, then enter h, b. Subtract second output from first for area.

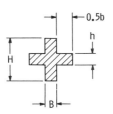

Enter 1.0 on the B'/B line in Fig. 17.17. Enter B/H to determine $f(I/c)_1$ and then b/H to determine $f(I/c)_2$. Add these to determine the section modulus.

For area, select rectangle symbol in Fig. 17.16. Then enter H, B value and then h, b value. Add these outputs to determine area.

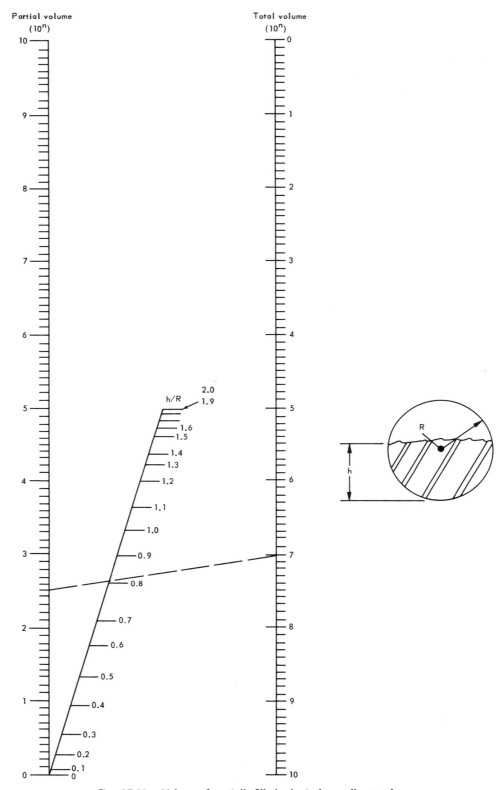

Fig. 17.11.   Volume of partially filled spherical propellant tank

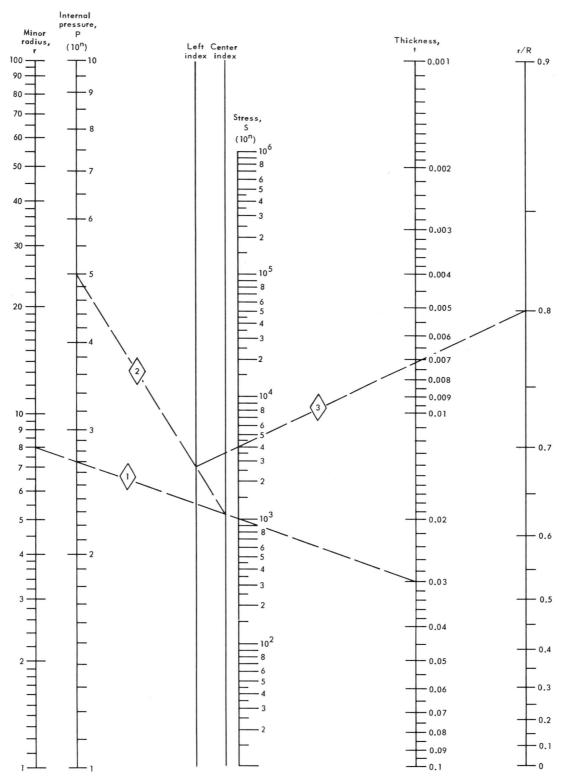

Fig. 17.12. Stress for toroidal tanks

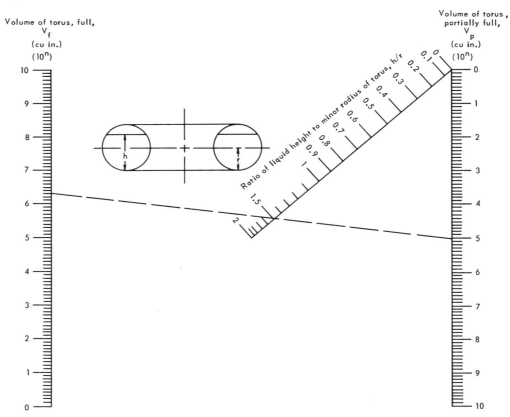

Fig. 17.13. Volume of torus, full and partially full

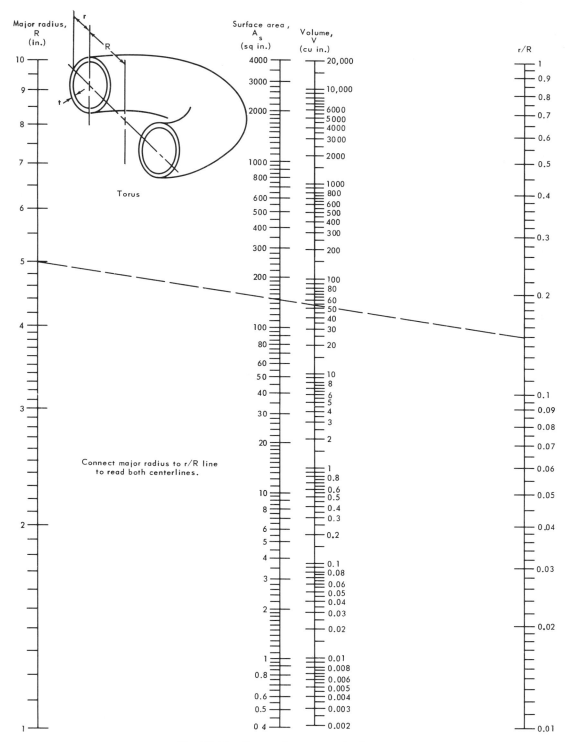

Fig. 17.14. Torus surface area and volume

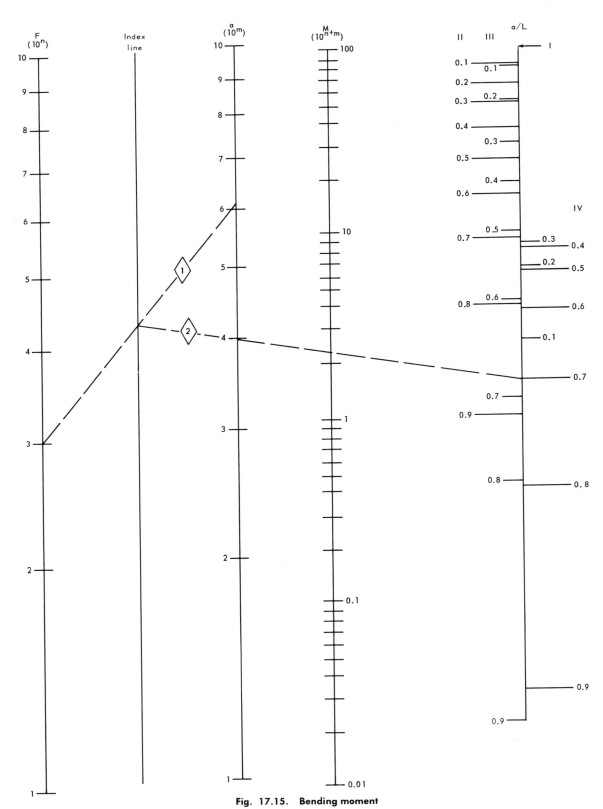

Fig. 17.15. Bending moment

See Table 17.1 for significance of point I and columns II, III, and IV.

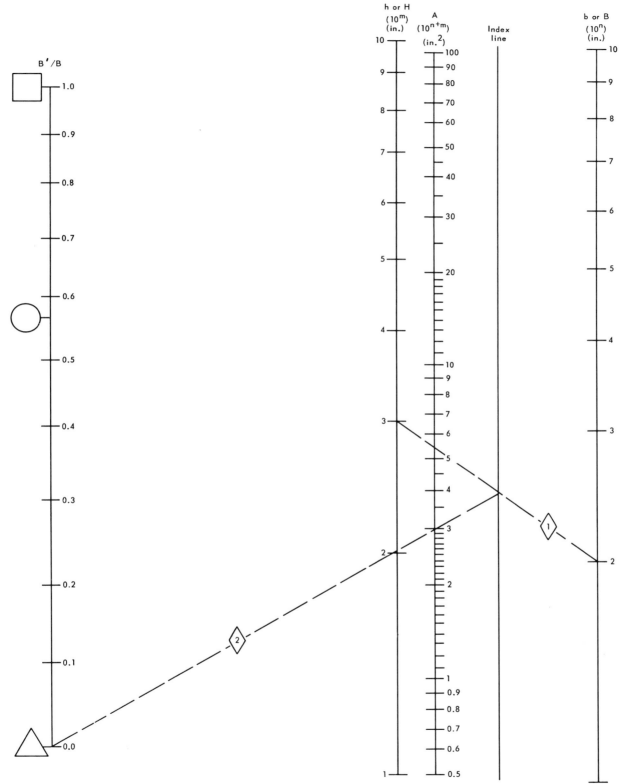

Fig. 17.16.   Beam cross section area

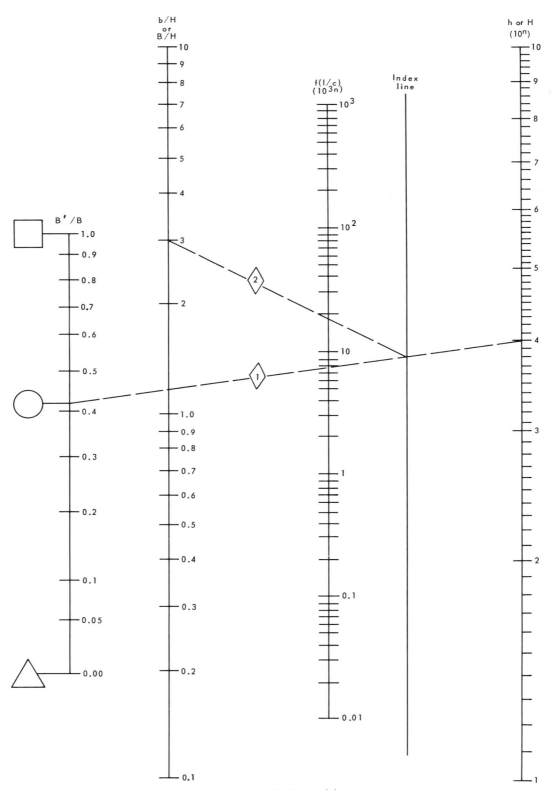

Fig. 17.17. Section modulus

Enter h when using b/h. *Enter H when using* B/H.

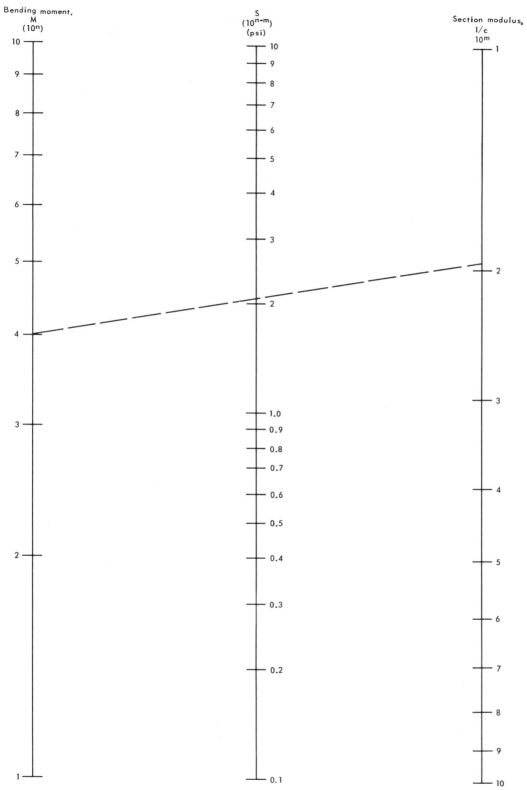

Fig. 17.18. Bending stress

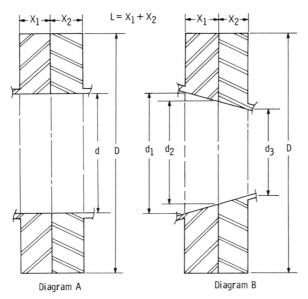

Fig. 17.19. Flanges

Stress may be estimated by means of Figs. 17.3, 17.4, and 17.5. The pressure considered in these charts may be internal, or it may be external as in regenerative nozzle cooling. Bending stress may be determined from Fig. 17.6.

Chamber volume and surface area may be determined from Figs. 17.7 and 17.8. Nozzle surface area may be determined from Fig. 17.20. These areas may be used in preliminary cooling design.

Weight may be estimated from Fig. 17.19 by entering values of A_s and t. Weight of coatings (such as ablative or heat protective) may be estimated by entering t as the coating thickness. Chamber weight may also be estimated by means of Fig. 9.15.

Solid rocket case design

Efficient design of a rocket is subject to the inert weight factor of which case weight can be a significant portion. For illustrations of case design, see Figs. 6.9 and 7.22. Reduction of case weight through higher strength-to-weight ratios and other means is

paramount in design. End-burning grains subject cases to a maximum of heat exposure whereas perforational grain design can utilize the propellant as an insulator. Exposure to hot gases and the duration of such heat transfer are among the determining factors in case design. The case is most often a pressure vessel designed to hold the grain and its combustion products, but in some exotic designs, such as autophagous rockets or case-consumable units, the case may be an integral part of the grain. A case cast of a material intended to be burned during the tail-off phase obviously would be subject to different parameters than the standard pressure-vessel combustion chamber.

The case, or combustion chamber, is a pressure vessel (see Fig. 17.10) subject to temperature conditions and internal pressures.

The thin wall formulation

$$S = DP_{max}/(D - d) \qquad (17\text{-}1)$$

where

D = outer diameter
d = inner diameter
P = maximum pressure

gives the maximum stress for thin wall chambers. The wall thickness may be initially approximated by

$$t_w = (D - d)/2 = DP/2s \qquad (17\text{-}2)$$

However, effective weakening of the case by fore end and aft head shapes and welds must be considered. This may be done rapidly by making use of Figs. 17.3, 17.4, and 17.5. The use of these charts is explained in the following steps.

1. Determine basic longitudinal or hoop stress from Fig. 17.3. This stress value is close to actual stress and may be found by using either the ratio of internal to external radii on line r/R or the wall thickness and outer radius on lines T and R respectively.

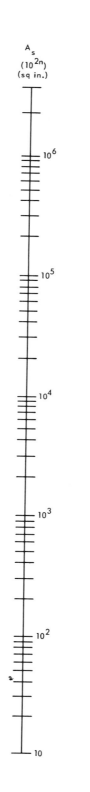

Fig. 17.20. Nozzle surface area from throat to exit.

If the ratio of radii is used, the appropriate value is entered on line r/R, the internal pressure is selected on line P, and the stress line is intersected by connecting these values. If the wall thickness and outer radius are used, these values are entered on lines R and t, and line r/R is intersected by connecting them (step 1). The r/R value determined by this indexing is then used to connect with the internal pressure (step 2) to index the stress value. The hoop stress is read from the right side of line S and the longitudinal stress is read from the left side.

2. Determine the longitudinal stress from Fig. 17.4 if the cylinder is welded longitudinally (see table 17.3).

3. Determine the cylinder head stress from Fig. 17.5 if applicable. (Filament wound plastic cases do not exhibit such variations.) First connect the type of head with the type of weld, thereby indexing the index line (step 1), and then connect this value with the appropriate stress on the extreme right line (step 2). The effective stress (including the stress increase) may now be read from line S_e.

Maximum pressure must be determined as a result of a total study of the pressure

Table 17.3   Weld coding

Code	Type of weld
1-A	Fully radiographed double weld, butt joint
1-B	Spot-examined double weld, butt joint
1-C	Not spot-examined double weld, butt joint
2-A	Fully radiographed single weld, butt joint with backing strip
2-B	Spot-examined single weld, butt joint with backing strip
2-C	Not spot-examined single weld, butt joint with backing strip
3	Single weld, butt joint without backing strip
4	Double full-fillet lap joint
5	Single full-fillet lap joint with plug welds
6	Single full-fillet lap joint without plug welds
1-A	Forged, not welded
1-A	Single filament, integral wound fiberglass-plastic, not welded.

complex. The maximum pressure in rocket design must be considered thoroughly since weight must be minimized for optimization. Hence stress must be computed with close tolerances. Safety factors in highly optimized solid rockets approach unity.

An additional pressure function must be considered in spin-stabilized rockets. The maximum pressure increase due to spin may be estimated by

$$K_p = (D - d)\, d\, (w)^2\, d_m / 4g \qquad (17\text{-}3)$$

where

w = rate of spin
d_m = material density.

APPENDIX A

How to Use Nomographs

The nomographs in this volume provide a systematic method of solving both simple and complex equations and problems not reducible to equations. Engineering data provides the basis for empirical graphs. Alignment charts provide for multiplication, division, and other computational processes including logarithmic calculations. Problems in differential and integral calculus are also resolved. Using a series of nomographs in the required order will lead to the solution of complex design systems.

The simplest form of the alignment chart is the three-line, single-step graph illustrated in Diagram A. If the user knows any two of the values, the third may be determined in one step by connecting the known values with a straight line to intersect the third value on the other line.

For example, in Diagram A if we know that the value of "a" is 5 and the value of

"c" is 6, we select 5 on the left line and 6 on the right line. Placing a straight edge across these values intersects the center line, "b," at 7.

If the center line is slanted as in Diagram B or irregular or curved as in Diagram C, the same procedure is followed. As an example, if "b" is 14 and "e" is 7 in Diagram B, a line connecting these values intersects "a" at the answer, 2.

More complex graphs contain more lines, but the procedure is the same. The unknown is found by entering the known values and connecting them with lines.

Diagram D illustrates a two-step graph. Such a graph commonly uses a reference, or index, line as a basis for taking the second step. To determine "c," first enter the values of "a" and "b" and intersect the reference line, I, by connecting these values. Then

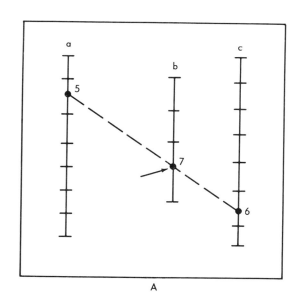

A

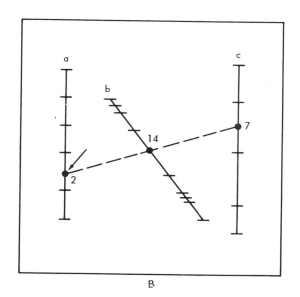

B

227

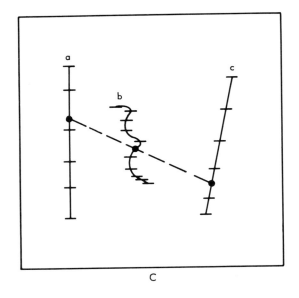

C

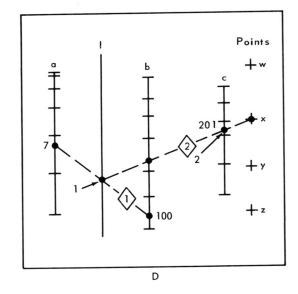

D

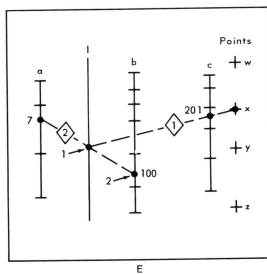

E

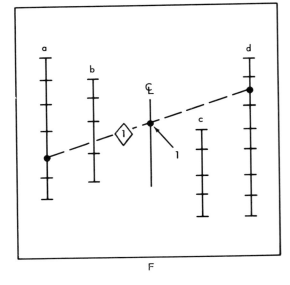

F

connect this point with the appropriate point (*w*, *x*, *y*, or *z*) at far right to produce the answer on line "c."

If "a" or "b" is unknown and "c" is known, the order is reversed as illustrated in Diagram E.

A common type of the alignment chart is the five-line graph with either a centerline or an index to one side. When three values are known, such as "a," "b" and "d," normally the step-by-step numbers on the chart will indicate which parameters to enter first, in this case "a" and "d." Connect these points to intersect the centerline as illustrated in Diagram F. Next select "b" on the line to the left of the centerline. Then connect this value with the point on the centerline, as illustrated in Diagram G, to intersect the answer on line "c."

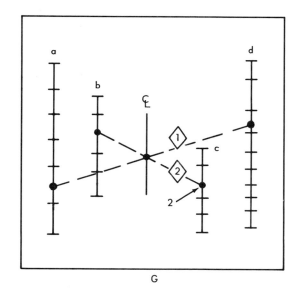

G

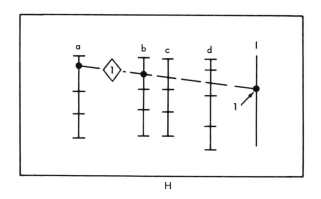

H

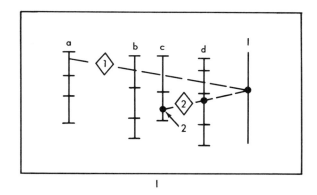

I

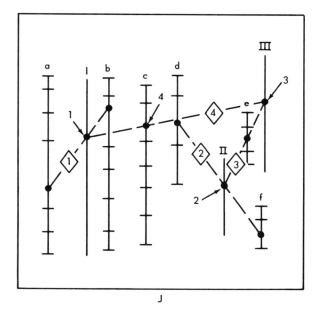

J

If the reference line is to one side, as shown in Diagrams H and I, the methods used are the same as in Diagrams F and G.

More complex graphs (Diagram J) are used similarly. When used in other than the numbered manner, that is for an unknown other than the one indicated, the known values are entered and the same lines are connected, although in a different order.

APPENDIX B

Nomograph Reference Table

To determine a desired value, first locate the parameter in the left column; then look for the known variables in the center column. The nomograph to be used will be listed in the corresponding right column. Figure numbers begin with the chapter number.

TO OBTAIN	FROM	USE FIGURE
A_c	A_t, P_c, C_w, c, n, d_p	6.6
A_c	$\dot{W}, r, d_p$	6.7
A_c	$\dot{r}, r, d, \dot{W}$	16.7
A_e	A_t, γ, P_c, P_e	2.5
A_e	$h, \Delta F$	5.2
A_s	R, L	17.8
A_s	R, r	17.14
A_t	$C_w, \dot{W}, P_c$	2.3
A_t	C_f, F, P_c	2.1
A_t	A_e, γ, P_c, P_e	2.5
A_t	A_c, P_c, C_w, n, c, d_p	6.6
C_d	Configuration	13.5
C_f	I_r, γ	2.11
C_f	I_{sp}, C_w	2.4
C_f	A_t, F, P_c	2.1
C_p	T_c	3.2
C_p	γ	3.4
C_w	I_{sp}, C_f	2.4
C_w	$A_t, \dot{W}, P_c$	2.3
C_w	M_o, T_c, γ	2.7
d	T	10.3
d	$V, f, L, A, \Delta P$	11.9
d	$\dot{W}, Q$	12.1
d	H, P	12.2
d_f	T	10.10
d_f	T	10.3
d_f	$\dot{r}, d_p, d_o$	10.2
d_f	$\dot{W}, r, \dot{r}, A_c$	16.7

TO OBTAIN	FROM	USE FIGURE
d_p	T	10.3
d_p	Propellant	6.4
d_p	c, A_t, A_c, P_c, C_w, n	6.6
d_p	$\dot{W}, r, A_c$	6.7
d_p	$\dot{r}, d_f, d_o$	10.2
D	$\dot{W}, d_m, P, S, V, T_1, \lambda$	12.14
D	u, N	12.7
D	hp, rpm, S	12.15
D	L, V, S, d_m	12.17
D	S, T, M	12.16
D	A, S	14.3
D	Re, $\dot{W}, \mu$	14.4
D_e	A, S	14.3
D_e	D_t, A_s	17.20
D_t	D_e, A_s	17.20
f	$f', F(k)$	11.8
f	$V, d, L, A, \Delta P$	11.9
f	T_c, M_o, L_c, γ	15.3
f	f_{Lc}, D_c, L_c	15.4
f	L, a, b, t	15.5
f	r, t	15.6
f	f_s, T	15.7
f	R, t	15.8
f	A_e, A_t, L, t	15.10
f	D_c, L_c, t	15.12
f	L, T	15.13
f	R, h, g	15.14
f	R, h, g	15.15

TO OBTAIN	FROM	USE FIGURE	TO OBTAIN	FROM	USE FIGURE
f	r, L	15.16	I_{sp}	I_r, T_c, M_o	2.10
f'	$\dot{\phi}_m, Z, \text{Re}, \dot{W}, \mu$	11.6	I_{sp}	P_c, propellant	6.2
f'	$f, F(k)$	11.8	I_{sp}	Propellant	6.3
			I_{sp}	$f(I_{sp})_1, \dot{r}, \dot{r}_{(opt.)}, P_c$	10.1
F	$\dot{W}, I_{sp}$	2.2	I_{sp}	$\dot{r}$, propellant	10.5
F	A_t, C_f, P_c	2.1			
F	F_x, A_t, A_{tx}	9.11	k	C_p, Pr, μ	14.5
F	F_m, W_x, W_m, L_x, L_m	9.12	k	$D, h_c, \text{Re}, \gamma$	14.6
$F(k)$	f', f	11.8	k	$D, \dot{W}, h_c, C_p, \mu$	14.7
$F(k)$	D_c, A	11.7	k	h_w, t_w	14.9
$f(P)$	P_e, P_c, γ	2.8	K_p	T_c	3.1
$f(P)$	I_r, γ	2.9	K_v	V_i, V_{es}	1.4
$f(R)$	h, celestial body	1.5	K_v	T, T_e	1.8
$f(R)$	T, V_s, celestial body	1.6	K_v	$f(R'), f(R)$	1.9
$f(R)$	V_s, celestial body	1.7			
$f(R)$	$K_v, f(R')$	1.9	M	F, a, L	17.15
$f(R)$	g, celestial body	1.11	M_o	C_w, T_c, γ	2.7
			M_o	T_c, I_r, I_{sp}	2.10
h	$f(R)$, celestial body	1.5	M_o	t_s, V_c, A_t, T, γ	11.3
h	$q, \Delta T$	14.1	$\dot{M}_p$	M_i, I_{sp}, V	1.1
h_r	h_c, T_c	14.8			
h_c	k, D, Re, γ	14.6	n	$A_t, A_c, P_c, C_w, c, d_p$	6.6
h_c	$D, \dot{W}, k, C_p, \mu$	14.7	n	c, P_c, r	6.8
h_w	k, t_w	14.9	N	N_s, Q, H	12.5
			N	u, D	12.7
H	$\sigma, (H_s)R$	12.3	N	hp, D_s, S	12.15
H	N_s, Q, N	12.5	N_s	S', σ	12.4
H	$\dot{W}, hp, \eta_P$	12.8			
H	P, d	12.2	P	$d_p, \dot{W}, W$	9.2
$(H_s)_R$	H, σ	12.3	P	H, d	12.2
hp	$\dot{W}, H, \eta_p$	12.8	P	R, r, S, t	17.3
hp	$f(P)$	12.15	P	r, S, R, t	17.12
hp	D_s, rpm, S	12.15			
			P_c	A_t, C_f, F	2.1
I/c	b, B', B, h, H	17.17	P_c	$A_t, C_w, \dot{W}$	2.3
I_r	$f(P), \gamma$	2.9	P_c	$P_e, f(P), \gamma$	2.8
I_r	T_c, M_o, I_{sp}	2.10	P_c	I_{sp}, propellant	6.2
I_r	C_f, γ	2.11	P_c	A_t, A_c, C_w, c, n, d_p	6.6
I_{sp}	W, V	1.1	P_c	c, r, n	6.8
I_{sp}	$F, \dot{W}$	2.2	P_c	$f(I_{sp})_1, \dot{r}, \dot{r}_{(opt)}, I_{sp}$	10.1
I_{sp}	C_f, C_w	2.4	P_c	R, r, S	17.3

TO OBTAIN	FROM	USE FIGURE	TO OBTAIN	FROM	USE FIGURE
Pr	C_p,k,μ	14.5	V	I_{sp},W,W_i	1.1
Pr	$\dot{W},C_p,h_o,A,\text{Re}$	14.10	V_c	A_t,t_s,M_o,T,γ	11.3
Pr	γ	14.6	V_{es}	V_s	1.3
			V_{es}	K_v,V_i	1.4
q	$h,\Delta T$	14.1	V_i	V_{es},K_v	1.4
q	$A,C_p,\Delta T,\dot{W}$	14.11	V_s	$T,f(R)$, celestial body	1.6
Q	N_s,N,H	12.5	V_s	$f(R)$, celestial body	1.7
Q	$\dot{W},d$	12.1	V_s	V_{es}	1.3
r	t,w	6.1	w	r,t	6.1
r	$\dot{W},d_p,A_c$	6.7	$\dot{W}$	F,I_{sp}	2.2
r	c,P_c,n	6.8	$\dot{W}$	A_t,C_w,P_c	2.3
r	$\dot{W},\dot{r},d,A_c$	16.7	$\dot{W}$	r,A_c,d_p	6.7
r_e	r (see Fig. 8.6), $Z,S,P_o,$ K_e,C_w,γ,A_p,d_p	8.7	$\dot{W}$	$\dot{W}_f,\dot{r}$	11.4
			$\dot{W}$	$\text{Re},\mu,Z,\dot{\phi}_m,f'$	11.6
$\dot{r}$	d_p,d_f,d_o	10.2	$\dot{W}$	d_m,D,P,S,V,T_1,λ	12.14
$\dot{r}$	$\dot{W},\dot{W}_f$	11.4	$\dot{W}$	$T_1,C_p,P_2,P_1,f(P),\eta$	12.12
$\dot{r}$	$r,d,A_c,\dot{W}$	16.7			
			$\dot{W}$	$\Delta P,f(P),d,\eta$	12.11
Re	$D,\dot{W},\mu$	14.4	$\dot{W}$	hp,H,η_p	12.8
Re	k,D,h_c,γ	14.6	$\dot{W}$	Q,d	12.1
Re	$\dot{W},C_p,h_o,A,\text{Pr}$	14.10	$\dot{W}$	$\Delta P,d,C_d,n,A$	13.6
Re	$\dot{W},\mu,Z,\dot{\phi}_m,f'$	11.6	$\dot{W}$	n,d,V,A	13.7
			$\dot{W}$	$C_p,h,A,\text{Pr},\text{Re}$	14.10
S_b	R,r,M	17.6	$\dot{W}$	$A,q,\Delta T,C_p$	14.11
S	R,r,P,t	17.3			
S	$M,I/c$	17.18	ΔT	$A,q,\dot{W},C_p$	14.11
S_e	S, type of weld	17.4	ΔT	h,q	14.1
S_e	S,α,h,R, type of weld	17.5			
S'	N_s,σ	12.4	ϵ	P_c,P_e,γ	2.5
			η	$T_1,C_p,P_2,P_1,f(P),\dot{W}$	12.12
t	r,w	6.1	η	$\Delta P,f(P),\dot{W},d$	12.11
t_s	V_c,A_t,M_o,T_c,γ	11.3	η_w	$\dot{W},N,W$	12.9
T	$V_s,f(R)$, celestial body	1.6			
T_e	K_v,T	1.8	μ	T	10.4
T_c	C_w,M_o,γ	2.7	μ	T_c	3.3
T_c	I_r,M_o,I_{sp}	2.10	σ	$H,(H_s)_R$	12.3
T_c	K_p	3.1	σ	S',N_s	12.4
T_c	C_p	3.2			
			$\dot{\phi}_m$	Re,f'	11.6
u	H,ψ	12.6	$\dot{\phi}_m$	Z, texture	11.5
u	D,N	12.7	ψ	u,H	12.6

APPENDIX C

Nomenclature

a Acceleration; (Chapter 17) distance to force on beam

a_e Acceleration at exit

A Area

A_c Burning area

A_{co} Initial burning area

A_e Exit area

A_p Port or duct area

A_{po} Initial port area

A_s Surface area

A_t Throat area

b Specific gas constant; (Chapter 17) minor beam width

B (Chapter 7) burning slope coefficient; (Chapter 17) major beam width

c Burning rate coefficient

$c*$ Characteristic velocity

C_d Flow coefficient

C_f Thrust coefficient

C_h Heat transfer coefficient

C_p Specific heat at constant pressure

C_v Specific heat at constant volume

C_w Weight flow coefficient

d Density or minor diameter

d_f Fuel density

d_m Material density

d_o Oxidizer density

d_p Propellant density

d_r Drill radius

D Diameter or effective diameter

D_c Chamber diameter

D_e Exit diameter or effective diameter

D_s Shaft diameter

D_t Throat diameter

e Base of natural logarithms

E Modulus of elasticity

f Friction factor or frequency; (as subscript) fuel

f' Friction prime factor

F Thrust

$f(k)$ Curvature friction factor function

$f(P)$ Pressure function

$f(R)$ Radius function

g Acceleration of gravity; (as subscript) grain

G Mass velocity

h Height; (chapter 17) minor beam height

h_a Height at apogee

h_c Conductive and/or convective heat transfer coefficient

h_o Coolant heat transfer coefficient

h_p Height at perigee

h_r Radiation heat transfer coefficient

h_t Total heat transfer coefficient

h_w Wall heat transfer coefficient

H Height, heat or head; (Chapter 17) major beam height

H_1 Inlet heat

H_2 Outlet heat

hp   Horsepower

$(H_s)_R$ Required suction head

I Total impulse

I_r Reduced specific impulse

I_{sp} Specific impulse

j (As subscript) exhaust

J Mass velocity function

k Thermal conductivity

k_1 Pressure constant

K Burning coefficient

K_e Erosive constant

233

K_g Coefficient of turbulence loss
K_i Transfer coefficient
K_n Ratio of full to empty mass or weight
K_o Transfer coefficient
K_p Equilibrium constant
K_v Orbit velocity constant
K_w Flow constant

L Length
L_c Chamber or case length
L_g Grain length
L^* Characteristic chamber length

m Mass or number of projections or tunnels; (Chapter 8) pressure exponent
m_o The harmonic
$\dot{m}$ Mass flow
M Mass, bending moment
M_i Inert mass
M_o Molecular weight
M_p Propellant mass

n Burning rate exponent
N Shaft speed
N_s Specific speed
Nu Nusselt number

p (As subscript) propellant or port
P Pressure or power
P_a Ambient pressure
P_c Chamber pressure
P_{cool} Coolant pressure
P_e Exit pressure
P_{ex} Exhaust pressure
P_g Grain pressure
P_o Fore end pressure
P_p Propellant pressure
Pr Prandtl number
P_{sg} Stagnation pressure in grain
P_{sn} Stagnation pressure
P_x Reference pressure or station pressure
P_1 Inlet pressure

q   Heat transferred per unit area
Q Total heat transferred; flow

r Linear burning rate
r_e Erosive burning rate
r_x Reference burning rate
$\dot{r}$ Fuel ratio
$\bar{r}$ Effective burning rate

R Radius or universal gas constant
R_e Exit radius
Re Reynolds number
R_g Grain radius
R_i Inner radius
R_o Body radius
R_t Throat radius

s Stress
s_b Bending stress
s_r Radial stress
s_t Tensile stress
S Perimeter or stress
S' Suction specific speed
S_o Initial burning perimeter

t Time
$t_{(lag)}$ Time lag
t_s Stay time
t_w Wall thickness
T Period or temperature; (Chapter 12) torque
T_c Flame or chamber temperature
T_g Grain temperature
T_p Propellant temperature
T_r Reference temperature
T_1 Inlet temperature

u Gas velocity, impeller tip speed, or velocity of propagation of wave

v Specific volume
V Velocity or volume
V_c Chamber or case volume
V_e Exit velocity
V_{es} Escape velocity
V_j Exhaust velocity
V_p Volume of propellant
V_s Orbit velocity

w Web thickness
w_1 Critical web distance
W Weight
$\dot{W}$ Weight flow
$\dot{W}_a$ Weight flow per unit area
W_f Fuel weight
$\dot{W}_f$ Fuel weight flow
W_i Inert weight
W_o Oxidizer weight
$\dot{W}_o$ Oxidizer weight flow
W_p Propellant weight

$\dot{W}_r$	Reference weight flow	ϵ	Ratio of exit to throat areas
$\dot{W}_x$	Instantaneous weight flow	η	Efficiency factor
		η_p	Pump efficiency
x	Coordinate	η_t	Turbine efficiency
y	Coordinate	η_w	Weight merit factor
z	Coordinate		
Z	Perimeter or distance from fore end	θ	Angle
Z_v	Sliver or sliver volume	λ	Wavelength or gaging coefficient
α	Nozzle half-angle or coefficient of thermal expansion	μ	Viscosity
β	Angle	ν	Poisson's ratio
Γ	Stress concentration factor	π	Pi (3.1416)
γ	Ratio of specific heats	σ	Suction parameter
Δ	Difference	$\dot{\phi}$	Surface texture function
ΔA	Area difference	ψ	Impeller tip speed coefficient
ΔT	Temperature difference	ω	Spin rate
ΔV	Velocity or volume difference	Φ	Loss function

Index